Advance praise for the book

'If you really want to know who we are, and how we got here, this is the book for you. A thrilling account of our extraordinary past – I couldn't put it down.' **Gurcharan Das**

'An amazing book, written in an engaging style . . . It grabs your interest from the first sentence.' **Bibek Debroy**

'At a time when the issue of the peopling of the planet by anatomically modern humans is becoming hotter and hotter, Tony Joseph has admirably cooled it down. He goes deep into recent developments in ancient DNA studies on human remains and delves into the issue of the "Aryan Migration". This is a vexing issue and not so easy to conclude. However, Joseph has marshalled multidisciplinary data from archaeology, linguistics, genetics and literature to support his stand on the issue. This is perhaps the most scientific way of presenting the Aryan debate. Lucidity is the hallmark of this book.' **Ravi Korisettar**

'Intellectual omnivore Tony Joseph offers an enjoyable meander through a minefield of how our ancestors got here.' **Pranay Lal**

'Masterful and unbiased reconstruction of human presence in India using evidence from archaeology, ancient and modern history, linguistics, geography and genetics, with a tilt on genetic evidence.' **Partha P. Majumder**

'Joseph deftly and brilliantly summarizes new findings of genetics that definitively solve old problems in South Asian history, and show we are all migrants and, ultimately, kin. A timely, fascinating and courageous book.' **Sheldon Pollock**

'There has been a lot of controversy about the origins of various populations, and in India, much of this is driven by a quasi-religious ideology. It is therefore refreshing to see how recent advances in DNA sequencing from people of various ethnicities as well as remains of ancient people is shedding light on the origins, migration and intermixing of people throughout history. In this very readable account, Tony Joseph has distilled the results of recent research and his book should be of interest to anyone curious about the waves of migration and intermixing that resulted in the rich tapestry that makes up the people of today's India.' **Venki Ramakrishnan**

'DNA studies of Indians dating to the millennia BCE confirm that they were a mixed population, and at a particular time included migrants from Central Asia. Given that these are initial studies their readings require circumspection when equating DNA identities with those from other sources. Tony Joseph's perceptive summary suggests how this new information might help clarify some of our understanding of the early past.' **Romila Thapar**

'Tony Joseph's book provides a remarkably accessible overview of the early stages of ancient Indian history, starting with the immigration from Africa of current humans to the age of the Vedas. He provides evidence from several fields of scientific enquiry, notably archaeology, linguistics, ancient texts and the very recent study of ancient genes (aDNA). The latter is currently revolutionizing ancient history not just of India but also of Europe, Africa and South America. Accordingly, T. Joseph lays to rest the question about the origins of the so-called (Indo-)Aryans and their settlement in ancient India – which has basically been politically motivated, especially for the past 40 years. As common in scholarship, not all individual scholars may agree on *all* questions and conclusions (such as the nature of the Indus civilization and its relation with the origin of the Dravidian speakers). However, finally, a firm basis for writing the history of ancient India is laid. The various sciences, in the end, lead us from darkness to the light of insight.' **Michael Witzel**

Early Indians

Early Indians

The Story of Our Ancestors and
Where We Came From

Tony Joseph

JUGGERNAUT BOOKS
C-I-128, First Floor, Sangam Vihar, Near Holi Chowk,
New Delhi 110080, India

First published by Juggernaut Books 2018

13

ISBN 9789386228987

The international boundaries on the maps of India are neither purported to be correct nor authentic by Survey of India directives.

The views and opinions expressed in this book are the author's own. The facts contained herein were reported to be true as on the date of publication by the author to the publishers of the book, and the publishers are not in any way liable for their accuracy or veracity.

Typeset in Adobe Caslon Pro by R. Ajith Kumar, Noida

Printed and bound at Nutech Print Services – India

To
My parents, for everything
My wife, who made this book possible
My daughter, who is the reason I wrote it

Contents

A Short Chronology of the Modern Human in Indian Prehistory

~ 300,000 years: The age of the earliest remains of a modern human, *Homo sapiens*, ever found – in a cave in Jebel Irhoud, about fifty kilometres from the city of Safi in Morocco.

~ 180,000 years: The age of the earliest modern human fossil found outside of Africa – at a rock shelter in Misliya in north Israel.

~ 70,000 years ago: Geneticists calculate that the earliest successful Out of Africa (OoA) migration happened around this time. This migration was termed 'successful' because these migrants are the ancestors of all of today's non-African populations. (Earlier modern humans outside of Africa have not left a lineage that is detectable today.) The OoA migrants 70,000 years ago are likely to have taken the Southern Route that would have brought them from Africa (specifically, from modern-day Eritrea and Djibouti) into Asia (modern-day Yemen) through Bab el Mandeb at the southern tip of the Red Sea.

~ 65,000 years ago: The OoA migrants reach India and are faced with a robust population of archaic humans. They perhaps take both an inland sub-Himalayan route and a coastal route, to keep themselves out of the way of other *Homo* species in the subcontinent who dominated central and southern India, and then move across the Indian subcontinent into south-east Asia, east Asia and Australia.

60,000–40,000 years ago: The descendants of the OoA migrants populate central Asia and Europe over this period.

~ 40,000 years ago: Neanderthals go extinct in Europe, with the Iberian peninsula in south-western Europe (modern-day Portugal and Spain) being their last refuge and stand.

45,000–20,000 years ago: The First Indians, the descendants of the OoA migrants in the subcontinent, start using Microlithic technology, and their population increases dramatically in central and eastern India. South Asia becomes the place where 'most of humanity' lives. Modern humans move into what would have been long-established refuges of other *Homo* species in southern and central India.

~ 16,000 years ago (14,000 BCE): Modern humans reach the Americas, the last major continent to be settled in by modern humans, after crossing Beringia, the land bridge between Siberia and Alaska.

~ 7000 BCE: In a village that is today called Mehrgarh, at the foot of the Bolan Hills in Balochistan, a new agricultural settlement begins that would ultimately become one of the largest habitations of its period between the Indus and the Mediterranean.

7000–3000 BCE: Migration of Iranian agriculturists from the Zagros region to south Asia leads to their mixing with the descendants of the First Indians sometime during this period. Geneticists estimate the mixing to have taken place at least by 4700 BCE to 3000 BCE.

7000–2600 BCE: The Mehrgarh site shows evidence for cultivation of barley and wheat, and increasing consumption of domesticated animals. The site was abandoned somewhere between 2600 BCE and 2000 BCE. By then agricultural settlements had spread all across north-western India – in the Indus and Ghaggar–Hakra river valleys and in Gujarat.

7000 BCE: From around this period there is evidence for rice harvesting and sedentary settlement at Lahuradewa in the Sant Kabir Nagar district of Uttar Pradesh in the Upper Ganga plain. The chronology of transition from harvesting wild rice to cultivating domesticated rice is not yet certain, but there is no doubt that Lahuradewa indicates experiments in agriculture were taking place at several places in south Asia around the same time and that Mehrgarh was not an isolated case.

5500–2600 BCE: The Early Harappan era, which witnesses early agricultural settlements growing into towns with their own unique styles, such as Kalibangan and Rakhigarhi in India and Banawali and Rahman Dheri in Pakistan.

3700–1500 BCE: Evidence of early agriculture starts to appear in different parts of India – eastern Rajasthan, southern India, the Vindhya region of central India, eastern India and the Swat valley of Kashmir.

2600–1900 BCE: The Mature Harappan period, which sees many sites being newly built or rebuilt, and many existing sites being abandoned. There is also a visible and higher level of standardization across the region, with a common script, seals, motifs and weights. The transition from the Early Harappan to the Mature Harappan phase happened over four or five generations, or 100 to 150 years.

2300–1700 BCE: The period of the Bactria–Margiana Archaeological Complex (BMAC), a civilization centred on the Oxus river (also called Amu Darya) and covering today's northern Afghanistan, southern Uzbekistan and western Tajikistan. The BMAC had close trade and cultural relations with the Harappan Civilization.

2100 BCE: A southward migration of pastoralists from the Kazakh Steppe, towards the southern central Asian regions that would today be called Turkmenistan, Uzbekistan and Tajikistan. The migrants make an impact on the BMAC, but mostly bypass it and move towards south Asia throughout the second millennium BCE, as listed below (2000–1000 BCE).

2000 BCE: Two major waves of migrations with their origin in China – after it had gone through the farming revolution and the resultant population surge – reshape south-east Asia. The first one brings Austroasiatic languages, new plants and a new variety of rice to India after 2000 BCE.

2000–1000 BCE: Multiple waves of Steppe pastoralist migrants from central Asia into south Asia, bringing Indo-European languages and new religious and cultural practices.

1900–1300 BCE: The Late Harappan period that sees the decline and eventual disappearance of the Harappan Civilization, primarily due to the effects of a long drought that affected civilizations in west Asia, Egypt and China as well.

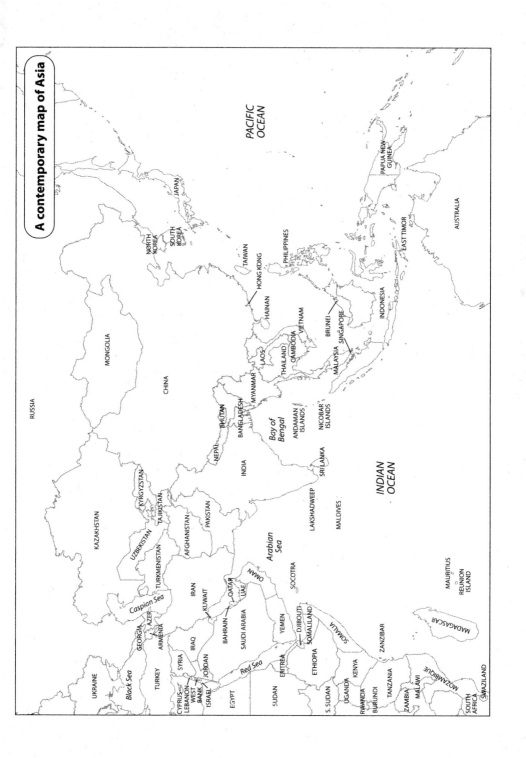

A contemporary map of Asia

Introduction

How We, the Indians, Came to Be

The story of our ancestors, the early Indians, who came from Africa, west Asia, east Asia and central Asia and made this land theirs over the last 65,000 years.

'But have you ever considered how fast you are really moving when it seems you are not moving at all?'

Professor Andrew Fraknoi, astronomer

Things are often not what they seem. As you read this sentence, perhaps sitting in a comfortable chair in your study, you would probably consider yourself at rest. But you are really not, because the Milky Way galaxy of which you are a part is moving through space at 2.1 million kilometres an hour. And that is without taking into account the effects of the earth's rotation on its own axis (1600 kilometres an hour at the equator and zero at the poles), its orbiting around the sun (107,000 kilometres an hour) and the sun's journey around the Milky Way (792,000 kilometres an hour).[1]

---

[1] Andrew Fraknoi, 'How Fast Are You Moving When Sitting Still', in *Universe in the Classroom* (Astronomical Society of the Pacific, 2007).

So in the roughly twenty seconds that it would have taken you to read the paragraph above, you have already moved thousands of kilometres without even knowing it!

Each successive discovery that led to the calculations above – that the earth is just one of many planets circling the sun; that the sun is just an average, middle-aged star in the Milky Way galaxy; that the galaxy itself is just one of at least a hundred billion galaxies – made some humans feel a little smaller while the wiser ones felt a new sense of awe at the size and majesty of what we are all a part of.

And this is true not just in a cosmic sense, but in a biological sense as well. Ever since Darwin shocked humanity a century and a half ago by formulating the theory of evolution and suggesting that our closest living relatives could be chimpanzees, every subsequent discovery has gone on to destroy the special status we had generously given ourselves previously. First, we thought that when we, the modern humans or *Homo sapiens*,[2] arrived on the scene, there was a sudden and appreciable difference in the kind of tools that were being made, as well as an efflorescence of artistry and abstract thought. Now we know that all that was conceit, and that the tools made by us and those made by our closest evolutionary cousins – *Homo erectus*, *Homo neanderthalensis*, Denisovans – were often indistinguishable from each other and that there was no watershed moment. All these extinct members of the *Homo* species (*Homo sapiens* being the only surviving member of the *Homo* family today) also had large brains like us.

In the past decade, we even learned that they were close enough to *Homo sapiens* genetically for us to have mated with them and

---

[2] Modern humans and *Homo sapiens* are used synonymously throughout this book. Humans, by contrast, could mean any member of the *Homo* species, such as *Homo habilis*, *Homo erectus*, *Homo neanderthalensis* or *Homo sapiens*. Archaic humans refers to those members of the *Homo* species that are extinct – such as *Homo habilis*, *Homo erectus* or *Homo neanderthalensis*. However, in the Holocene (from ~9700 BCE onward), 'humans' will mean modern humans since archaic humans are believed to have gone extinct by then.

Homo erectus (lived approximately 1.89 million to 143,000 years ago in parts of Africa and Asia)

Homo heidelbergensis (lived approximately 700,000 to 200,000 years ago in parts of Africa, Asia and Europe)

Homo neanderthalensis (lived approximately 400,000 to
40,000 years ago in Europe and south-western and central Asia)

produced children who grew up to be fertile. We know this because
all non-African *Homo sapiens* today carry about 2 per cent Neanderthal
genes in their DNA. Some of us – like the Melanesians, Papuans and
Aboriginal Australians – also carry 3 to 6 per cent Denisovan DNA.
Because of this genetic inheritance, we may call them our ancestors, but
it is perhaps more reasonable to see them as our evolutionary cousins
with whom *Homo sapiens* did dally. Biologically, we are just a part of a
gradual continuum of evolution, with chimpanzees sharing 96 per cent
of *Homo sapiens* DNA. And the emergence of *Homo sapiens* itself was
not a single, dramatic episode. It was a slow process, involving several
beginnings and intermixing of various members of the *Homo* species,
all of them now extinct. For the small-minded among us, this would
be a forgettable, if not an unacceptable, fact. For the rest, this would
be yet another reason to appreciate the life around us, and wonder at
the unity that binds all life together so tightly.

What applies to cosmology and biology applies to our history as well. In the rather short history of *Homo sapiens* (just around 300,000 years, compared to the 3.8 billion years that there has been life on earth), each of our tribes, clans, kingdoms, empires and nations have considered themselves to be of superior status. Some thought that they were the children of a special God, others that they were the chosen people, and still others that they were divinely ordained to rule over everyone else. People also thought that the spot of earth they occupied was at the very centre of it all – for example, the Middle Kingdom of the Chinese or the 'Midgard' (Middle Enclosure) of Norse mythology. The new nationalisms of the eighteenth and nineteenth centuries built on all these ideas to make everyone believe that the newly created 'nations' they belonged to were infinitely superior to all other nations, and that they had always existed, from 'time immemorial'! In fact, 'time immemorial' is the phrase we hear most often when we try to grasp our deep history.

None of these beliefs are true, of course. No human community is of exceptional status relative to others. None are children of God, or chosen people, unless all are. And none of us live upon the centre of the earth any more than we live on its periphery, since we live on the surface of a globe. Nations as we understand them today are no older than a few centuries, and we are all interconnected – genetically, culturally and historically – far more than we imagine. And even 'time immemorial', it turns out, can increasingly be pinned down, dated, analysed and grasped. And when we do that, we get a far better understanding of our society and culture, and what went into their making.

Would this be upsetting to some? You bet. It is like being told the secrets of the magician who held you spellbound in your childhood. When you learn his secrets, you can either bemoan your lost innocence and the ruined charm of the magic, or you can revel in your new knowledge, the clarity it brings to many things and the possibilities of what you could do with it. This book is betting that you, dear reader, are of the second kind.

In the chapters that follow, we will be looking at how and when modern humans, or *Homo sapiens*, first arrived in India; what evidence they left behind for us to see; who their descendants are today; who else followed them as migrants to this land of ours; how and when we started farming and building the world's largest civilization of its time; when and why this civilization declined; and what happened next.

This book is about prehistory, and prehistory is about the period that comes before history. History begins when writing begins and places and individuals come alive before us, with their own names and, sometimes, recognizable stories. In prehistory there are no written records and hence we cannot know for sure the names of people and places or the stories of individuals. But, to some extent, we can work out what the life of people might have been like back then, using other kinds of evidence. The evidence in prehistory comes from fossils, archaeological excavations of ancient human settlements, various objects made by humans, like tools, and, increasingly importantly, the DNA of both ancient and present-day individuals.

So where does India's prehistory end and history begin? This is a tricky question because we have written records on seals and tablets from the Harappan Civilization that thrived between 2600 BCE and 1900 BCE, so in a sense we can say that is when our history begins and prehistory ends. But we have not yet deciphered the Harappan script and, therefore, have no knowledge of what is written in those records, so that period falls outside of history and within prehistory. But then, we do have some references to the Harappan Civilization in the contemporary records of the Mesopotamian Civilization in west Asia, so that makes it part of history again.

It is this ambiguity that prompted some historians to use the label 'proto-history' to describe the period between prehistory and history. In this book, we will come right up to the tail end of the Harappan

Civilization and a few centuries after that, leaving the rest for another book, perhaps!

Why this book now

There is a reason why this book could have been written only now, and not earlier. It is because our understanding of deep history has changed dramatically in the last five years or so. Large stretches of our prehistory are being rewritten as we speak, based on analysis of DNA extracted from individuals who lived thousands or tens of thousands of years ago. Many 'facts' that we took for granted have been proved wrong, and many questions left dangling in the air as historians, archaeologists and anthropologists argued it out among themselves have been given convincing new answers – thanks to the recently acquired ability of genetic scientists to successfully extract DNA from ancient fossils and then sequence it to understand all that bound people together, or distinguished them from each other. If technology had not matured to the level it has, scientists would not have been able to make the discoveries they are making today. And if it were not for their latest findings, our prehistory would have remained as vague and contentious as earlier and this book would not have been written.

Just to get a sense of the speed at which things have moved, consider this: when work on this book began six years ago, we did not know who were the people of the Harappan Civilization or where their descendants had gone, but now we do. Six years ago, we did not know how much of our ancestry we owed to the original Out of Africa migrants who reached India about 65,000 years ago, but now we do. Six years ago, we did not know when the caste system began, but now we can zero in on the period with a fair degree of genetic accuracy. These are just a few examples that demonstrate our rapidly improving understanding of prehistory, and not only with regard to India.

Here's a short list of things that have changed about human

prehistory in other parts of the world because of ancient DNA: we now know that large portions of European populations were replaced not once but twice within the last 10,000 years. First, a mass migration of farmers from west Asia around 9000 years ago mixed with or replaced already established hunter-gatherers in Europe. And then a mass migration from the Eurasian Steppes about 5000 years ago mixed with or replaced the then existing population of European farmers. In the Americas, we now know that native American populations, before the arrival of Europeans, owed their ancestry to not one but at least three migrations from Asia. In east Asia, we know that much of the ancestry of people in the region derives from two or more major expansions of populations from the Chinese agricultural heartland. In 2010 we learned that modern humans had interbred with Neanderthals and in 2014 we learned that our ancestors had interbred with Denisovans (a member of the *Homo* species that was identified only because of ancient DNA sequencing) as well.

When this journey began six years ago, though, I did not know that the field I was getting into, prehistory, was just about to experience an explosion of new knowledge. That is something that happened serendipitously. When I started, I was fascinated by the Harappan Civilization and the questions that were still unsettled: who were the people who built the largest civilization of their time, and where did they go? I visited Harappan sites from Dholavira and Lothal in Gujarat to Rakhigarhi in Haryana, which led me on to many meetings and email discussions with leading historians, archaeologists, epigraphists, linguists and geneticists both in India and from around the world – Romila Thapar and B.B. Lal in New Delhi; Sheldon Pollock in New York; Michael Witzel, David Reich and Vagheesh Narasimhan in Harvard; Iravatham Mahadevan in Chennai; Martin B. Richards in Huddersfield, UK; Peter Underhill in Stanford; M.K. Dhavalikar, V.N. Misra, Vasant Shinde and K. Paddayya in Pune; Shereen Ratnagar in Mumbai; Ravi Korisettar in Dharwad; Partha Majumder in Kolkata; K. Thangaraj in Hyderabad;

Lalji Singh in Varanasi; Niraj Rai in Lucknow; Michael Petraglia in Jena, Germany . . . the list is long.

Not all of them agreed with each other, and while every discussion answered some of my questions, it left me with even more questions, not just about the Harappan Civilization but also about the periods preceding it. Before I knew it, the question I was dealing with had morphed from who were the Harappans to how we, the Indians, came to be.

Somewhere along this route, it became clear that the most important revelations were coming from the new field of population genetics. This led me on a search for population genetics papers dealing with the peopling of south Asia – and there were dozens of them – often followed by meetings or discussions with the authors. I met K. Thangaraj, principal scientist at the Centre for Cellular and Molecular Biology (CCMB), Hyderabad, and Lalji Singh, former head of CCMB and, later, vice chancellor of the Banaras Hindu University, Varanasi. This was in 2015 and I was hoping to publish my first story about the Harappan Civilization and the issue of 'Aryan migrations'[3] based on these conversations and the research. But there was a problem. I could not complete my article because what Singh and Thangaraj told me did not match up with what I read in the paper they had authored along with other scientists from around the world in 2009.[4] I, therefore, decided to put the story on hold and gain a better understanding of

---

[3] 'Aryan migration' refers to the theory that Indo-European languages, including an early version of Sanskrit, were brought to India by migrants from the Eurasian Steppes, who called themselves Aryans, sometime after 2000 BCE. 'Aryan' is the self-description of a group of people speaking the same family of languages. Wherever the phrase 'Aryan migration' is used in this book, it has to be read as the short version of 'migration of Indo-European-language-speaking people who called themselves Aryans'. And wherever the word 'Aryan' is used, it has to be read as 'people who called themselves Aryans'.

[4] David Reich, et al., 'Reconstructing Indian Population History', *Nature* 461: 489–94 (September 2009).

population genetics before writing anything on it. Then, two years later, in 2017, I came across a paper titled 'A Genetic Chronology of the Indian Subcontinent Points to Heavily Sex-biased Dispersals', co-authored by Professor Martin B. Richards of the University of Huddersfield in the UK along with his team.[5] I read this paper again and again till things started slowly falling in place. I finally got a grip on the issue and could zero in on what was causing the disconnect.

The confusion arose because when I met the scientists in 2015, they had put forward a new hypothesis to me that did not figure in their 2009 paper. This hypothesis was that there were no large-scale migrations to India during the last 40,000 years or so. They also said that there were two very ancient populations, one located in north India and the other in south India and that all of today's populations had descended from the mixing of these two groups, technically given the tags Ancestral North Indian (ANI) and Ancestral South Indian (ASI).

But the paper that Lalji Singh and Thangaraj had co-authored with scientists from the Harvard Medical School in 2009 (titled 'Reconstructing Indian Population History') had made no claims about there having been no large migrations to India in the last 40,000 years. The paper had clearly stated that ANI, unlike ASI, were related to west Eurasians (west Asians, Europeans, central Asians and people of the Caucasus region). This would have given strong support to the theory that Indo-European-language speakers who called themselves Aryans had migrated to India within the last 4000 years or so, after the Harappan Civilization started declining. The issue of 'Aryan migration' has been a political hot button for decades, with many opposing the suggestion that 'Aryans' were late migrants to the country, not part of the earliest Indian population. There was the additional problem of the Harappan Civilization: if this mighty civilization which has left an indelible imprint on India preceded 'Aryan migrations', then that cuts at the root of the right-wing position that the 'Aryans', Sanskrit

---

[5] Marina Silva, et al., 'A Genetic Chronology . . .', *BMC Evolutionary Biology* (2017).

and the Vedas are the fundamental wellspring of Indian culture. (See also the section 'The second method: Whole genome data' in chapter 2, p. 87.)

The paper co-authored by Martin B. Richards was published on 23 March 2017 and I found it a week later. I spent the following two months reading and rereading tough-to-understand genetics papers from different time periods dealing with the formation of the Indian population; trying to correlate their often contradictory findings with the state of development of population genetics when each of these papers was written; getting in touch with the authors of these papers, many of them doyens of their field with many path-breaking discoveries to their credit; and checking and double-checking the conclusions I was arriving at; and reading more and more papers.

On 17 June 2017, *The Hindu* published my article 'How Genetics Is Settling the Aryan Migration Debate'. Here, I explained how DNA evidence supported the theory that Indo-European-language speakers who called themselves Aryans had migrated to India from central Asia around 4000 years ago. The statements made in that story were reconfirmed in March 2018 by a path-breaking paper written by ninety-two scientists from around the world, 'The Genomic Formation of South and Central Asia', and posted in the preprint server for biology, bioRxiv. Reich and Thangaraj were among the co-directors of the study. The scale of the study and the fact that it was based on ancient DNA made the findings far more robust and the chronology of migrations far more accurate.

My experiences during the writing of this book have taught me that even in the most professional of settings, personal preferences can play a part in how research findings are interpreted. And often it may not be a question of bias, but a genuine belief that the truth might cause harmful side effects and, therefore, needs to be treated cautiously. For instance, there could be a fear that the fact of Steppe migrations may reinvigorate old divisions of language and region, just as there might have been a fear among some Indian historians over half a century ago that details of medieval atrocities might cause enmity between different religions. But in reality, holding back the truth cannot heal divisions. It can only cause them to fester underground with even more vigour. Also, no scientist or writer can accurately predict the consequences of a particular truth being withheld: history is made up almost entirely of unintended consequences. So the only reasonable position for any scientist, or any writer for that matter, to take is to let the facts speak, but make sure that no unsupported conclusions are drawn from them.

In this case, it is true that there was large-scale migration of Indo-European-language speakers to south Asia in the second millennium BCE (you will read more about this in chapter 4), but it is also true that all of today's population groups in India draw their genes from several migrations to India: there is no such thing as a 'pure' group, race or caste that has existed since 'time immemorial'. Of course, the degree to which the mixing between different populations has occurred differs across regions and communities. So the fact of Indo-European migrations has to be told along with the truth of multiple migrations and large-scale population mixing that happened over millennia. We are today a uniquely Indian civilization that has drawn together many population groups with different migration histories, and its impulses, culture, traditions and practices come from multiple sources, not just one singular source.

In the pages that follow, we will use the new findings made possible by ancient DNA as well as the latest fascinating discoveries made by archaeologists, anthropologists, epigraphists (people who study ancient inscriptions), linguists, palaeoscientists (scholars of the geologic past) and historians to peel the layers of our ancient past one by one. It is a fascinating story and one that is rarely told. Come along.

1

The First Indians

How a band of Out of Africa migrants found their way to India, dealt with their evolutionary cousins and a range of environmental challenges, mastered new technology, made this land their own and became the largest modern human population on earth.

If you want to get as close as possible to the lives of the first modern humans in India, one of the best places to go to is Bhimbetka in Madhya Pradesh's Raisen district, about forty-five kilometres from the state capital, Bhopal. It is an enchanting place spread over seven hills and full of naturally occurring rock shelters that are perhaps more imposing and majestic than most man-made residences of the twenty-first century. There are perennial springs, creeks and streams filled with fish; plenty of fruits, tubers and roots; deer, boar and hare; and, of course, as many quartzite rocks as you need to make all the tools you want. Moreover, the elevation of the hills makes it possible for the residents to keep track of who is approaching them: food or predator, nilgai or leopard!

In the world of early humans, this must have been the equivalent of a much sought-after luxury resort. Ever since it was first occupied some 100,000 years ago, it has never lain vacant for too long, and it is easy to imagine there having been a long waiting list to get in. A place so well liked that millennia after millennia, one or the other *Homo* species, including our own ancestors, the *Homo sapiens*, lived and hunted and painted and partied there. Yes, the rock shelters are full of paintings, including some that depict people dancing to drumbeats. The paintings are not well-dated, so it is quite likely that most of them, though not all, were made within the last few thousand years, rather than many tens of thousands of years ago. But there are a few petroglyphs, or rock carvings or markings, that could be the earliest evidence of art created by members of the *Homo* species anywhere in the world – a few perfect cupules (small cup-like depressions) with lines beside them.

A rock shelter in Bhimbetka

Perfect cup-like depressions made on the walls of a rock shelter in Bhimbetka.
This is perhaps the earliest evidence of art made by members of the
Homo species anywhere in the world.

But do we know exactly when the first modern humans set foot in Bhimbetka or, for that matter, in India? The answer to that is a bit complex. First we need to define what we mean when we say 'first modern humans in India'. The technical meaning of the phrase would be any individual belonging to the *Homo sapiens* species who set foot in India first. However, when we say 'first modern humans in India' we also often mean to say the earliest direct ancestors of people living in India today. It is important to know that there is a difference between the two.

For example, let us say the first *Homo sapiens* in India were a group of thirty people in Bhimbetka 80,000 years ago. Let us also say that some calamity – like the huge Toba supervolcanic eruption

Tony Joseph

Paintings on the wall of a rock shelter in Bhimbetka,
perhaps a few thousand years old

that occurred in Sumatra, Indonesia, 74,000 years ago and impacted
the entire region from east Asia to east Africa – directly or indirectly
killed off every one of this first group of modern humans, leaving
behind no one to populate the subcontinent.[1] Let us then imagine a
second group of modern humans in Bhimbetka around 50,000 years
ago, who successfully settle down and leave behind a lineage of people
still found in India. Are we referring to the second group when we
say the 'first modern humans in India'? This may look like a matter of
semantics and it is so, in a way, but it has meaningful implications for
us when we interpret archaeological or other evidence to understand
the history of early Indians.

---

[1] This is a hypothetical scenario. Recent research suggests the impact of the volcanic
eruption on life in the region was not as severe as earlier understood.

If you ask Indian archaeologists when the first modern humans arrived in India, at least some of them are likely to put a date that is perhaps as early as 120,000 years ago. But if you ask a population geneticist, that is, a geneticist studying genetic variations within and between population groups, the answer is likely to be around 65,000 years or so ago. This seemingly irreconcilable difference between the two sciences is not necessarily contradictory. When geneticists talk about the first modern humans in India, they mean the first group of modern humans who have successfully left behind a lineage that is still around. But when archaeologists talk about the first modern humans in India, they are talking about the first group of modern humans who could have left behind archaeological evidence that can be examined today, irrespective of whether or not they have a surviving lineage.[2]

Did we really have to come from elsewhere?

But why do we assume that modern humans arrived in India from elsewhere at all? Why couldn't they have originated right here? Until a few decades ago, this would have been considered a reasonable question, because the theory that modern humans evolved in different parts of the world separately, from archaic or extinct members of the *Homo* species such as *Homo erectus* that had spread out all over Eurasia by about 1.9 million years ago, was still prevalent – even though Charles Darwin had suggested the African origin of modern humans as early as in 1871. The theory was that the later intermingling of very differently evolved populations kept us together as one species, thus preventing us from branching off into different species in different continents.

---

[2] Not all archaeologists agree with this distinction, though. 'This idea of successful and failed dispersal is also under scrutiny,' says the archaeologist Ravi Korisettar, adding, 'All dispersal events are successful.'

But this theory has now gone into the dustbin and no serious scientist anywhere puts this forward as a possibility any more (though there may be some isolated holdouts especially in China which, till very recently at least, was wedded to the idea of indigenous, independent evolution of the Chinese people from archaic humans). The reasons why this theory went into disuse are both archaeological and genetic. The fossil record of Africa is rich with the remains of our closest relatives – *Sahelanthropus tchadensis* 7 million years ago, *Ardipithecus ramidus* 4 million years ago, *Kenyanthropus platyops* 3.5 million years ago, *Homo habilis* 2.4 million years ago and *Homo heidelbergensis* 700,000 to 200,000 years ago – and there is no other region in the world that comes anywhere close to it. But the clinching argument against multiple origins of humans on different continents is genetic. The DNA evidence has been conclusive that modern humans outside of Africa are all descendants of a single population of Out of Africa (OoA) migrants who moved into Asia sometime after 70,000 years ago and then spread around the world, perhaps replacing their genetic cousins such as *Homo neanderthalensis* along the way. All recent discoveries have gone on to reaffirm the African origins of all modern humans. As recently as in June 2017 came the news that an ancient skull from a cave in Jebel Irhoud, about fifty kilometres from the city of Safi in Morocco, has been classified as belonging to the *Homo sapiens* species and was dated to about 300,000 years ago.

Until the Jebel Irhoud fossil was dated and classified, the oldest discovered modern human fossils were two skullcaps dated to about 195,000 years ago, found at the archaeological site of Omo Kibish in Ethiopia. So the Jebel Irhoud discovery takes back modern human origins by about 100,000 years and also removes any remaining doubt about where we came from. Though the skull from Jebel Irhoud looks quite like us in its facial traits, the back of the skull is elongated like that of archaic humans and it also has 'very large' teeth, suggesting that the modern human didn't emerge suddenly and fully formed, but was a work in progress as early as 300,000 years ago.

The logic of genetics

But even if you accept that modern humans arose in Africa, how did the geneticists arrive at the conclusion that all non-African populations descend from a single Out of Africa migration that happened less than 70,000 years ago? One needs to know a little bit of genetics to follow their argument. Genetics can sound somewhat complex to anyone who hasn't paid attention to it earlier, but it is worth investing a few minutes to get familiar with it. You will be able to follow the story even without a perfect understanding of the mechanics of the science described here, so don't get hassled if the explanations given here are not clear enough. Once you get more familiar with the vocabulary, you can come back and read this part again. So here we go.

Almost all the genetic code that humans need is packed into twenty-three pairs of chromosomes that we all carry inside the nuclei of our cells. There is one exception and that is the mitochondrial DNA, or mtDNA, which stays outside the cell nuclei. Each person inherits his or her mtDNA exclusively from his or her mother (the father also carries mtDNA passed on by his own mother, but he doesn't pass it on to any of his children, male or female). The twenty-three chromosomes together with the mtDNA comprise a person's genome.

Unlike the mtDNA, each of the twenty-three pairs of chromosomes in the cell nuclei has one half contributed by the mother and the other by the father. The two chromosomes that make up each pair are similar to each other, carrying similar codes at similar locations. But they are only similar, not identical. The differences between the chromosomes contributed by each of our parents usually amount to about 0.1 per cent. This is the same as the difference between the genomes of any two individuals, on average. These differences arise because of mutations, or random errors that happen especially during cell division – a necessary part of reproduction in living things. These mutations are then passed down through generations – assuming that, on balance, they are not harmful and, therefore, not weeded out by natural selection.

You could look at a genome as a genetic code written using an 'alphabet' of just four chemicals – A (adenine), C (cytosine), G (guanine) and T (thymine) – and if you do that, then each genome is made up of about three billion individual letters.[3] A 0.1 per cent difference between the genomes of two people translates to about three million differences between the two genomes. If the two genomes came from people who shared a recent ancestor, then the differences would be smaller (which also means that genetic differences can be used as a measure of how close or distant two individuals are genetically).

Notice that although each person carries twenty-three pairs of chromosomes inherited from their parents, they pass on only twenty-three chromosomes (not twenty-three pairs of chromosomes each) to their children. How does this happen? The genetic term for this is recombination and what this means is that each parent randomly shuffles and divides the twenty-three pairs of chromosomes they inherited from their own parents and then passes on only one set of twenty-three chromosomes to their child. In other words, each parent does not pass on all of the genetic material they inherited from their own parents. They pass only twenty-three chromosomes each, thus together giving their offspring a complete set of twenty-three pairs of chromosomes.

---

[3] According to the National Human Genome Research Institute, 'A chromosome is the structure housing DNA in a cell . . . DNA is a remarkably simple structure. It's a polymer of four bases – A, C, T, and G – but it allows enormous complexity to be encoded by the pattern of those bases, one after another.' Pieces of DNA, or strings of code, that lead to observable traits such as height or eye colour are called genes.

But there is one exception to this rule: the twenty-third chromosome pair, or the sex chromosomes. Sex chromosomes are what makes a person male or female. If a person carries two sex chromosomes of the type XX, the person will be female, and if the person carries two sex chromosomes of the type XY, the person will be male. For a series of complex reasons, the Y part of the sex chromosome that every male carries comes directly from his own father, with no recombination. In other words, in the case of a male, the Y-chromosome he carries in his sex chromosome comes exclusively through the paternal line going back hundreds of thousands of years.

So we could say, up to an extent, that the Y-chromosome – or Y-DNA, as it is sometimes called – is a mirror image of the mtDNA, which is inherited exclusively through the maternal line, going back hundreds of thousands of years. If the Y-chromosome comes from your father and his father and his father and so on, the mtDNA comes to you from your mother and her mother and her mother and so on. Where the parallel breaks is in the fact that while both men and women carry mtDNA, only men carry the Y-chromosome. Since women's sex chromosomes are of the XX type, they do not have the Y-chromosome at all. There's a reason for this apparent lack of symmetry. Within every cell, mtDNA performs an extremely critical function – it has the code to convert chemical energy from food into a form that cells can use. No wonder mtDNA is often called 'the powerhouse of the cell'. So to put it plainly, no man can do without the mtDNA, but every woman can do without the Y-chromosome.

This nature of the Y-chromosome and mtDNA – that they are inherited without recombination and trace the exclusively paternal and exclusively maternal lines of a person – has proved to be of enormous help, especially in the early stages of population genetics, in understanding the migration history of individuals and populations. What made this possible were mutations, or copying errors, as we discussed earlier. If the mtDNA of a person were exactly the same as her mother's, grandmother's and so on, or if the Y-chromosome of a man were exactly the same as his father's, grandfather's and so on, there would be no substantive information or insight to be had by analysing anyone's mtDNA or Y-chromosome. But mutations that accumulate over time ensure that the Y-chromosome or mtDNA of a person carries the genetic track record of all that happened in the exclusively paternal or maternal lineage of that person.

For example, if Great-Grandmother had a mutation called PCX on her mtDNA, then she would have passed that on to all her daughters and all her granddaughters born to her daughters and so on. And if you are doing genetic testing of a population in a particular area and come across multiple cases of PCX on the mtDNA, you would be able to create a genetic tree for people with that mutation – and all other mutations that followed since then, if any. In other words, if you have the mtDNA or Y-chromosome of a person, you will be able to locate that person's maternal or paternal lineage over time. Since global human genetic databases exist for both the Y-chromosome and the mtDNA, it is now possible to locate where in the world people who belong to the same group or mutation are currently widely present.

But that is not all either. Scientists have long noticed that there is a certain pattern or regularity in mutations. This is not an exact science but still, they have worked out mutation rates with large confidence margins for the whole genome, as well as for specific regions of the genome such as the Y-chromosome and mtDNA.

While the track record of mutations as reflected in the mtDNA and Y-chromosome allows us to create genetic family trees, the mutation rate allows us to work out the approximate time that has passed since two branches or sub-branches of a tree diverged.

Population geneticists have given names to the branches of the global mtDNA and Y-chromosome family trees that they have created using extensive genetic studies. The equivalent word in population genetics for a branch is haplogroup – haplo means single in Greek, so haplogroup means single group.[4] While a parent branch is called macro-haplogroup, subhaplogroup or clades refers to sub-branches. Some of the oldest branches in the mtDNA genetic tree are haplogroups L0, L1, L2 and M7, while some of the oldest Y-chromosome branches are A, B, CT and D. So by identifying the mtDNA or Y-chromosome haplogroup of a person, you can broadly work out his or her long-term paternal or maternal lineage, and how close or far other lineages are from this. If two people belong to the same mtDNA haplogroup, it means they have a common female ancestor dating from the time that haplogroup originated. And if two men belong to the same Y-chromosome haplogroup, it means they share a common male ancestor dating from the time that haplogroup originated.

A caveat is in order here. Remember that the Y-chromosome or mtDNA that you carry is only a small, less than twenty-third part of your entire genome. So just figuring out your Y-chromosome or mtDNA doesn't say much about what your entire genetic make-up is: it just tells you who your entirely paternal or entirely maternal ancestors are. And they are just a small part of the people you can legitimately call your ancestors. Your mother's father, or your father's mother, or your father's mother's father, for example, are all left out in the cold if you go only by Y-chromosome or mtDNA lineages. If you go back ten generations, you will have 1024 people whom you can call your ancestors, but your mtDNA or Y-chromosome would have any connection with only ten of them. If you go back fifteen generations, the number of your ancestors goes up exponentially to 32,768, but your mtDNA or Y-chromosome would be connected to only fifteen of them! This could sometimes lead to odd results.

---

[4] This is a reference to the fact that the Y-chromosome and mtDNA are haploid – inherited from a single parent, without mixing with the DNA of the other parent. This is unlike the rest of the chromosomes, which are diploid, or inherited from both the parents.

For instance, it is possible for a person to be almost entirely of Chinese ancestry, but to belong to a Y-chromosome haplogroup that is common only in India. All that would have been necessary for this to happen is for an Indian man to have left behind a son in China, say, ten centuries ago and for this son in turn to have founded a lineage with every generation having at least one son, all of whom lived in China and married Chinese women. A male descendant of this lineage today – the son of the son of the son . . . of the Indian – could still carry the Indian man's Y-chromosome, but he would be of Chinese ancestry for all practical purposes, because there is only one tenuous, centuries-old link that connects him to India.

So while the mtDNA and Y-chromosome are helpful ways to understand population movements or histories of individuals or groups, they may not be sufficient to grasp a person's or a population's entire genetic make-up or its relationship to other populations. For that,

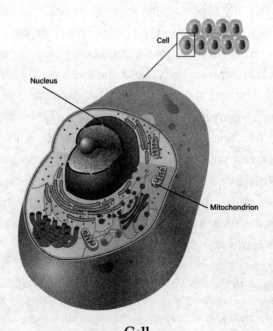

Cell
Source: National Human Genome Research Institute, Bethesda

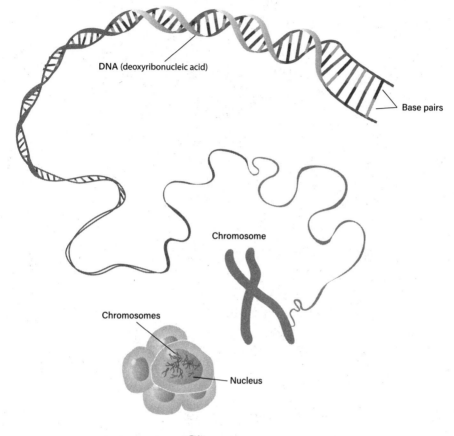

DNA (deoxyribonucleic acid)

Base pairs

Chromosome

Chromosomes

Nucleus

Chromosome
Source: National Human Genome Research Institute, Bethesda

we need whole genome sequencing, which studies a person's entire genome, not just the Y-chromosome or the mtDNA. We cannot create genetic trees out of the twenty-two non-sex chromosomes – which are called autosomes – because recombination, or the shuffling and division of genes, makes that impossible. But whole genome sequencing can clearly help measure the degree of affinity between different population groups. Whole genome sequencing used to be a very costly and time-consuming affair earlier, but with improving technology, it is becoming increasingly common in genetic studies.

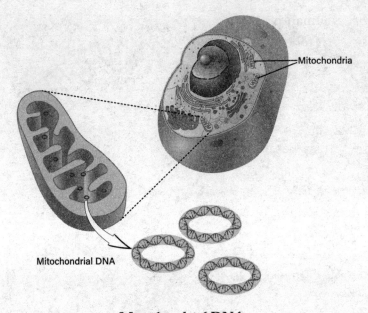

Mitochondria

Mitochondrial DNA

Mitochondrial DNA
Source: National Human Genome Research Institute, Bethesda

Dating 'Out of Africa'

Now that the basic mechanics of genetics is out of the way, let's tackle the next question: why do geneticists say that all modern humans outside of Africa come from a single group that migrated out of that continent, and why do they put the time of the exodus to 70,000 years ago or later? The reason is straightforward. When you look at the mtDNA of people outside of Africa all around the world, you will find they all descend from a single haplogroup with deep lineage in Africa, namely, L3. Think about what this means: that all people outside of Africa are descended from a single African woman who originated the L3 mtDNA haplogroup! Africa has about fifteen other, much older, lineages with names such as L0, L1, L1a and L1c, but none of them were part of the group that went on to populate the rest of the world. L3 has two immediate descendant lineages or subhaplogroups today, M and N, with N having its own major subhaplogroup, R. Thus all of the human population in the world outside of Africa carries lineages that follow from M, N or R. While south Asia has all three of these haplogroups, Europe has only two of them, N and R, with M missing.

The picture is much the same when you look at Y-chromosome lineages as well. There are only three haplogroups from Africa that went on to populate the rest of the world – C, D and F, all deriving from a parent haplogroup called CT. Again, this means that all humans outside of Africa are descended from a single man who started the Y-chromosome haplogroup CT. What these facts show is that only a subsection of the modern human population in Africa moved out to populate the rest of the world. Secondly, the fact that all the migrating mtDNA haplogroups descended from L3 and not any of the other haplogroups suggests that the migration event was single and not multiple, because multiple migration events would probably have resulted in present-day populations deriving their ancestry from a larger number of mtDNA haplogroups, not just L3. The likelihood that multiple migrations all happened to have the same L3 lineage is very, very small.

How do we then arrive at a dating of 70,000 years ago or later for the migration event itself? That is also straightforward. By using mutation rates and present-day genome data, geneticists can calculate the time of the emergence of particular haplogroups. They have concluded that L3 emerged approximately 70,000 years ago. Similarly, the N lineage is dated to 61,000 years ago and M to 48,000 years ago. So the Out of Africa event couldn't have been much later than 61,000 years ago (otherwise there would have been N lineages in Africa, which is not the case), and it couldn't have been much earlier than 70,000 years ago, because otherwise there would have been no L3 lineage in Africa at all, which is not the case either.[5]

---

[5] There is low frequency presence of N and M in Africa today, but this is usually attributed to back-migration from Eurasia after the OoA event.

This may seem like a neat argument that zeroes in on the period of the exodus, but these estimates are based on 'average' ages of the haplogroups we are interested in. The actual range for each of those calculations could be a few thousand years on either side. So it is more reasonable to say that the OoA event couldn't have happened later than about 50,000 years ago and earlier than about 80,000 years ago. And out of this rather large range, if we take certain specific climatic considerations into account on top of genetic ones, we arrive at a window of roughly between 50,000 and 60,000 years ago.

The right climate

This is because the period before about 57,000 years ago, up to about 71,000 years ago, was glacial, when the climate was cold and arid and it would not have been the best time for anyone to attempt moving continents. During the ice ages, large bodies of water are locked up in ice sheets, and the cooler weather means there is less evaporation from the sea and hence less rain and more aridity.

Animals expand into new areas mostly during warmer, wetter periods, when new lakes and waterbodies form where there used to be none, and deserts start turning into lush new grasslands. Herbivores such as cows, goats, sheep and deer move into these new areas in search of plenty and safety and, soon enough, the predators, including *Homo sapiens*, follow the herds looking for abundant food. So if you are trying to identify the time for a major migration, it would be advisable to check the climate cycles – though, of course, critically, there are exceptions in this too, as there are in everything else. Some migrations may indeed have been facilitated by arid, cold climates that shrank the lakes and seas separating continents or regions, and thus made crossing them easier.

Geologists in the 1960s and 1970s discovered a way to figure out the chronology of global climate fluctuations by drilling the deep sea to get sedimentary cores and then looking at the oxygen isotope data that these contained at different depths. High levels of Oxygen-18 represent cold, glacial periods and low levels of Oxygen-18 represent warmer, wetter periods. Based on this, we can now look back at the climatic history of the world for the past many millions of years, which has been divided into periods called Marine Isotope Stages (MIS). Currently we are in MIS 1, a warm, wetter period that began about 14,000 years ago and is still continuing. Odd-numbered MIS stages are all warm and wet, while even-numbered MIS stages denote cold and dry glacial periods.

Marine Isotope Stages (MIS)	Start date ('000 years ago)
MIS 1	14
MIS 2	29
MIS 3	57
MIS 4	71
MIS 5	130
MIS 6	191
MIS 7	243
MIS 8	300
MIS 9	337
MIS 10	374
MIS 11	424
MIS 12	478
MIS 13	528
MIS 14	563
MIS 15	621
MIS 16	676
MIS 17	712
MIS 18	761
MIS 19	790
MIS 20	814
MIS 21	866

The list continues to MIS 104, beginning 2.614 million years ago.

It is from this MIS data that we know that the climate changed around 57,000 years ago, making for a warmer, wetter world when the deserts of north Africa and the Arabian peninsula were transformed into lush green grasslands, inviting both herbivores and carnivores, including our own ancestors, from the refuges of sub-Saharan Africa. The period before that, 71,000 to 57,000 years ago, was a glacial age classified as MIS 4 when the greenery and the grasslands receded along with the herbivores and the carnivores and deserts returned to being deserts again. The period even before that, 71,000 to 130,000 years ago, was warm, but this mostly falls outside the broad genetic range for OoA. So if the OoA migration did take place during a warm, wet period, then we can say it happened roughly between 60,000 and 50,000 years ago.

You will have noticed by now that while the logic flows easily and there is an overall chronological range that seems robust, the specific times arrived at are fluid rather than firm, with enough room for adjustment. New archaeological or genetic discoveries could shift them this way or that, within the broad range, as geneticists adapt to newer and more granular information.

At the gates of Asia

So far we have been looking at the genetic and climatic sides of the OoA migration story. When we come to archaeology, however, we see things in a slightly different light for reasons explained earlier: genetics mostly focuses on people who left behind a lineage while archaeology looks at people who left behind archaeological evidence, even if not a lineage (this difference between the two disciplines could disappear soon though, as archaeologists and geneticists get their hands on more and more ancient DNA of humans who may or may not have living descendants).

In January 2018, for example, archaeologists announced that

upper jaw teeth belonging to a modern human discovered in Misliya in north Israel had been dated to 180,000 years ago, making it the earliest human fossil found outside of Africa ever. The Misliya site was a rock shelter frequently used by archaic or extinct members of the *Homo* species for hundreds of thousands of years, something like an even older version of our own Bhimbetka. Before the Misliya find, the earliest modern human fossils found outside of Africa were dated to between 80,000 and 120,000 years ago and these were also discovered in Israel, from the nearby Skhul and Qafzeh caves. All these dates are much earlier than the estimated period of OoA migration – between 50,000 and 60,000 years ago.

And it is not just in the Levant (modern-day Syria, Jordan, Lebanon and Israel) that modern human fossils that old have turned up. In April 2018 a team of archaeologists announced they had discovered a modern human finger fossil in the Al Wusta prehistoric lake in north-eastern Saudi Arabia, dated to about 88,000 years ago. This area is a desert now, but it would have been a well-watered and inviting habitat 88,000 years ago, with hundreds of freshwater lakes. 'We have found 10,000 ancient lakes in Arabia. We have visited about 200, and about 80 per cent have evidence of archaeology,' said Michael Petraglia of the Max Planck Institute of Germany, whose team made the discovery, in an interview to *National Geographic*.

Based on current evidence, it is becoming clear that modern humans started emerging in Africa around 300,000 years ago and they began their forays into the Levant by at least 180,000 years ago and into Arabia by at least 88,000 years ago. But the question remains: if modern humans were pushing through the gates of Asia as early as 180,000 to 88,000 years ago, why were these initial forays not successful in terms of leaving behind a lineage that filled out our world? Why did they have to wait till around 60,000 years ago or so before that became possible? Especially when you consider that our evolutionary cousin, *Homo erectus*, managed to move out of Africa and spread as far as south-east Asia as early as around two million years ago.[6] Probably other members of the *Homo* species also made their way out of Africa much before *Homo sapiens* did, leaving behind descendant species such as Neanderthals and Denisovans. So what stopped the first modern human explorers out of Africa in their tracks?

There are two likely answers to that question. One is, of course, climate cycles and the other, Neanderthals. The routes out of Africa into Asia probably closed or opened depending on whether the world was going through a cold, glacial period or a warm, interglacial period. The presence of Neanderthals is perhaps even more pertinent. The modern humans that moved into the Levant would almost certainly have come across the Neanderthals, the dominant species in Eurasia by then. There is plenty of archaeological evidence of their presence in the Levant around the same time as the modern humans were there.

Neanderthal remains have been found at the Tabun cave in Israel, close to Skhul, dated to 120,000 years ago, roughly the same period as when modern humans were there. They have also been found at the Kebara cave, not very far from the Skhul–Qafzeh caves, and have been dated to 61,000 to 48,000 years ago. So it is quite possible that modern humans found it difficult to progress into Eurasia from the Levant because they couldn't prevail over the Neanderthals who were well adapted to the colder climate of Europe. Our ancestors ultimately did prevail over the Neanderthals tens of thousands of years later in Europe itself, but it should be noted that the first encounters between us perhaps didn't go in our favour.

---

[6] Until about two million years ago, there was no Red Sea and animals could just walk across from Africa into Asia, or from Asia into Africa, all along the region that is today separated by the Red Sea. It is likely that *Homo erectus* was one of the last mammals to walk across from Africa to Asia through this route. The Red Sea was formed by the Red Sea Rift, caused by the divergence between the African plate and the Arabian plate. The rift started about two million years ago, and since then Africa has been moving away from Arabia at the rate of fifteen millimetres every year. It still continues to widen.

A proper understanding of what happened during the first attempts of the modern humans to break into Eurasia, however, is not possible without a grasp of both geography and climate. There were four possible paths for ancient modern humans out of Africa and into Eurasia – from Morocco in north-western Africa to Spain across the Strait of Gibraltar; from Tunisia into Sicily; from Egypt into the Sinai peninsula and on to the Levant; and from Eritrea in eastern Africa to Yemen and Saudi Arabia across the Bab el Mandeb at the southern tip of the Red Sea. Of these four possibilities, there is no evidence that the first or the second routes were ever used. But we have plenty of evidence that the third and fourth routes were used – whenever the climate allowed these routes to be open.

For much of what palaeoscientists call the Pleistocene (between 2.58 million and 11,700 years ago), the climate would have been very cold and the Sahara and the Sinai would have been deserts, making the route to the Levant from Egypt a difficult one. But thankfully, there were interglacials, or warmer periods (these are the oddly numbered MIS stages, as we discussed earlier), when the weather became wetter and the deserts became green and passable. During these periods, it would have been possible for both human and animal migrations to occur between Africa and Eurasia. The period between 243,000 and 191,000 years ago was an interglacial (MIS 7), a relatively warm period, and so was the period from 130,000 to 71,000 years ago (MIS 5). The recent Misliya fossil (180,000 years old) find comes broadly within the first period, while the Skhul–Qafzeh finds (80,000 to 120,000 years old) in Israel fall within the second period.

Whenever the warm interglacial periods ended and the climate cooled again, the Neanderthals already in central or northern Eurasia would perhaps have moved down to southern Eurasia in greater numbers in search of slightly warmer climes, putting pressure on the newly arrived *Homo sapiens* there. It is thus possible that the climate cycles and the presence of Neanderthals together are what scuppered

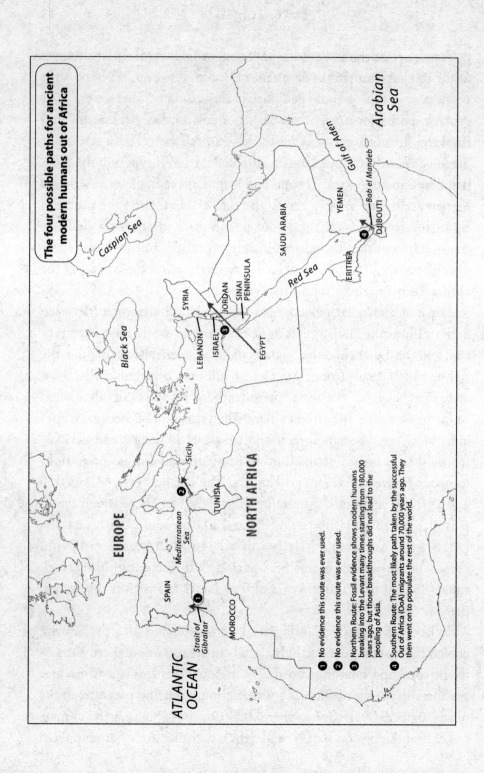

The four possible paths for ancient modern humans out of Africa

ATLANTIC OCEAN

EUROPE

Mediterranean Sea

Black Sea

Caspian Sea

Strait of Gibraltar

SPAIN

MOROCCO

TUNISIA

Sicily

NORTH AFRICA

SYRIA

LEBANON

ISRAEL

JORDAN

SINAI PENINSULA

EGYPT

SAUDI ARABIA

Red Sea

YEMEN

ERITREA

DJIBOUTI

Bab el Mandeb

Gulf of Aden

Arabian Sea

❶ No evidence this route was ever used.

❷ No evidence this route was ever used.

❸ Northern Route: Fossil evidence shows modern humans breaking into the Levant many times starting from 180,000 years ago, but those breakthroughs did not lead to the peopling of Asia.

❹ Southern Route: The most likely path taken by the successful Out of Africa (OoA) migrants around 70,000 years ago. They then went on to populate the rest of the world.

the attempts of the first modern humans to colonize the rest of the world from Africa through the Levant.

While we are using modern-day geographical descriptions to explain what happened, our ancient ancestors wouldn't have been thinking in terms of moving from one continent to another at all. They would have been merely expanding or contracting the range of their movements, as climate patterns changed and along with it the regional spread of the flora and fauna on which they depended. Dry, cold periods would have shrunk their range and warm, wet periods would have invited them, along with the animals they were hunting to eat, to newer pastures.

We do not know whether these early modern human occupants of the Levant managed to get back to Africa before the Sinai and the Sahara turned to dry deserts again or whether they just got cut off from Africa by these expanding deserts as the cold wave swept in, while also being hemmed in by the Neanderthals moving southward, and thus perished. What we do know is that after these first pieces of evidence of modern human presence in the Levant, we had to wait more than 30,000 years to see the next evidence of their presence in the region again, around 50,000 years ago – and this time, obviously, they survived.

Breakthrough at the Gate of Tears

While this was playing out on the Egypt to Levant route, usually called the Northern Route to Asia from Africa, there was action on the Southern Route too, which goes from Eritrea through Bab el Mandeb at the tip of the Red Sea, to Yemen and Saudi Arabia. (Bab el Mandeb means Gate of Tears. One legend attributes it to the cries of the drowned as an earthquake clove apart Asia and Africa, while another legend says it is simply a warning to travellers of the dangers of trying to cross the sea as it was full of reefs.)

Unlike the Northern Route, which does not involve any crossing of the sea, the Southern Route involves the crossing of the Red Sea at Bab el Mandeb – a distance of about thirty kilometres currently. But during glacial periods, when the climate is cold and dry, the sea level recedes, thus reducing the distance across the Red Sea to a third, making the crossing somewhat easier. There is no archaeological proof that modern humans of this age had figured out how to build boats, but it is possible that they had, because there is evidence that they had been leading a beachcombing lifestyle for thousands of years, living off marine resources such as fish and shells. Boats would have been a nice and natural addition to that lifestyle.

Whatever that may be, what we do know is that the cold and dry glacial periods that made life impossible for modern humans in the Levant may have been a little kinder on those making a move through the Southern Route. Not only because it made the Red Sea crossing easier, but also because once they crossed over to Arabia, the monsoons may have compensated somewhat for the dry aridity of the glacial ages at least in the coastal areas. (The monsoons are a side effect of the existence of the Himalayas, which were formed as a consequence of the Indian tectonic plate pushing into the Eurasian plate, beginning some fifty million years ago.)

So even during the coldest periods, some archaeologists posit, modern humans may have been able to cross into Asia at Bab el Mandeb. As we will shortly see, there is reason to be sceptical of the climatically deduced OoA migration window between 50,000 and 60,000 years ago. In fact, some archaeologists have been pushing for a much earlier migration out of Africa. Michael Petraglia is one of them. In 2012 he decided to back his convictions with an ambitious research project called 'Palaeodeserts', which focused on Saudi Arabia and intended to uncover ancient connections between Africa and the rest of Eurasia. It was under this project that the 88,000-year-old finger fossil was discovered at the Al Wusta prehistoric lake in north-eastern Saudi Arabia. Talking about the discoveries that were being made, Petraglia said in an interview to *Nature Asia*, 'The most amazing thing to me are the fossil finds. They say something about the kinds of animals that could migrate into Arabia. We have fossils of elephants; these are gigantic creatures, much larger than the African elephant. Amazingly, we also have hippos. These finds tell you something of how wet it really was. Because the hippos cannot survive in very arid and dry situations, so the environment had to be green for them to survive.'

Was the person whose finger was found in Al Wusta part of the successful migration that later went on to populate the rest of the world? Definitely not, because the dating of that fossil, at 88,000 years ago, puts it beyond the maximum range for OoA migration that geneticists have deemed possible. So it is likely that this early migrant was part of a group that perished, much like those in the Levant. Or to propose a more radical idea, perhaps a subsection of his group managed to escape the aridity of interior Arabia as the climate changed, made it to south Asia, and perhaps even managed to make it to south-east Asia and Australia over thousands of years, but all of them perished for a combination of reasons or perhaps mostly because of the Toba supervolcanic eruption, the most violent volcanic eruption in the past two million years, thus leaving behind no genetic trace in today's populations.

What Petraglia's findings in the Arabian desert prove is that the Southern Route was very much viable, and that it is almost certainly the route taken by those modern humans who went on to fill up the world at the time of the OoA migration.[7]

The Arabian chapter in the history of the first modern human

---

[7] Why is it not possible that *Homo sapiens* migrated to the Levant, say, around 60,000 years ago and mingled with Neanderthals, resulting in our current gene mix? The sequence of evidence of modern human occupation of the world does not support this. The earliest evidence for modern humans in Europe is around 45,000 years ago while they were in Australia at least by around 60,000 years ago. This suggests that the OoA migration happened through the Southern Route, reaching first Arabia, then south Asia, south-east Asia and Australia. If the peopling of the world had happened through the Northern Route, one would expect to see evidence of modern human presence in Europe much earlier than in east Asia or Australia.

migration is momentous for quite a different reason too. This is the most likely place where modern humans and Neanderthals first met, mated and left behind a genetic trail in all non-African modern human genomes that is still detectable today. All non-Africans carry about 2 per cent of Neanderthal genome.

There is no reason why this interbreeding couldn't have happened in different regions repeatedly. But it is simpler to assume that at least one mixing happened near where the first migrants broke out of Africa and before they split to go their different ways because that is the easiest explanation as to how all non-Africans came to possess a *similar* amount of Neanderthal DNA.

When this discovery of Neanderthal genes in humans was first announced in 2010, the world was shocked because until then we had considered Neanderthals quite inferior to us, and as belonging to a different species that would not have been able to reproduce with us. Now, of course, we know that we interbred not just with Neanderthals but with Denisovans as well, and that this may not be the full story either. In Africa and elsewhere too, research is throwing up the increasing likelihood that there were more interbreeding events between modern humans and our genetic cousins, some of whom we may not even have identified yet.

Now that we have taken the story out of Africa and into Asia, this may be a good time to bring in evidence from another part of the world that allows us to get a clearer picture of when the OoA episode took place and what might have happened after it. That part of the world is Australia, and it is a crucial element of any story about the first migrants. In June 2018 a team of scientists led by the archaeologist Chris Clarkson of the University of Queensland, Australia, established that humans were in that continent by between 59,300 and 70,700 years ago, or if you take the midpoint, by 65,000 years ago.

The scientists did this by careful dating of things left behind by modern humans in a cave in Madjedbebe in Australia's Northern Territory – things such as mortars, pestles, ground-edge axes and painting material. Since Australia has never been populated by any member of the *Homo* species other than *Homo sapiens*, there is little doubt that this was the work of our own species. In July 2018 another study led by Kira Westway of Macquarie University, in Sydney, declared that two teeth discovered from the Lida Ajer cave in Indonesia's Sumatra island a century ago had been securely dated to between 63,000 and 73,000 years ago, and that they belonged to modern humans. Together, these two studies have pushed back the date for modern human occupation of south-east Asia and Australia by 15,000 to 20,000 years and put severe constraints on both the timing of the OoA episode and the mode of migration.

Even if you take the lowest estimate of these two studies, it is clear that modern humans were in south-east Asia by at least 63,000 years ago. That means the OoA episode has to be outside the postulated range of 50,000 to 60,000 years ago. There are only two ways to square this circle. One, either the people who left behind fossils and tools at Madjedbebe and Lida Ajer were part of an earlier wave of migrants from Africa who failed to leave behind a genetic lineage, or the OoA episode happened much earlier than previously believed, even if this means modern humans crossed over to Arabia during a cold and dry glacial period rather than a wetter, warmer interglacial period. This would push the date for OoA closer to the absolute limit of genetic possibility for OoA at 80,000 years ago. Let us consider this option and see where it goes.

The race through Asia

What is a reasonable amount of time for hunter-gatherers to walk down from, say, Yemen to Australia, taking into account that they would not be walking with the intention to reach Australia, but merely to hunt, gather, eat and survive? There is no easy way of telling, but we do know from archaeological evidence that it took the first migrants to America (about 16,000 years ago) only a couple of thousand years

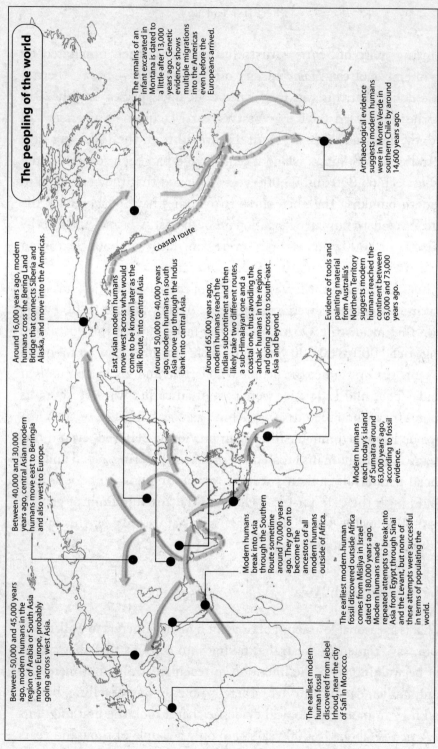

The peopling of the world

The remains of an infant excavated in Montana is dated to a little after 13,000 years ago. Genetic evidence shows multiple migrations into the Americas even before the Europeans arrived.

Archaeological evidence suggests modern humans were in Monte Verde in southern Chile by around 14,600 years ago.

coastal route

Around 16,000 years ago, modern humans cross the Bering Land Bridge that connects Siberia and Alaska, and move into the Americas.

East Asian modern humans move west across what would come to be known later as the Silk Route, into central Asia.

Around 50,000 to 40,000 years ago, modern humans in south Asia move up through the Indus bank into central Asia.

Around 65,000 years ago, modern humans reach the Indian subcontinent and then likely take two different routes, a sub-Himalayan one and a coastal one, thus avoiding the archaic humans in the region and going across to south-east Asia and beyond.

Evidence of tools and painting material from Australia's Northern Territory suggests modern humans reached the continent between 63,000 and 73,000 years ago.

Between 40,000 and 30,000 years ago, central Asian modern humans move east to Beringia and also west to Europe.

Between 50,000 and 45,000 years ago, modern humans in the region of Arabia or South Asia move into Europe, probably going across west Asia.

Modern humans reach today's island of Sumatra around 63,000 years ago, according to fossil evidence.

Modern humans break into Asia through the Southern Route sometime around 70,000 years ago. They go on to become the ancestors of all modern humans outside of Africa.

The earliest modern-human fossil discovered outside Africa comes from Misliya in Israel – dated to 180,000 years ago. Modern humans made repeated attempts to break into Asia from Egypt through Sinai and the Levant, but none of these attempts were successful in terms of populating the world.

The earliest modern human fossil discovered from Jebel Irhoud, near the city of Safi in Morocco.

Adapted from Stephen Oppenheimer, 'Out-of-Africa, the Peopling of Continents and Islands: Tracing Uniparental Genes Across the Map', Philosophical Transactions of the Royal Society B, The Royal Society Publishing, 2012 to reach the tip of South America from Alaska – a distance of about 21,000 kilometres. They probably moved down the coastal route on the western seaboard of the Americas. The beauty of a coastal route is that it makes the migration process faster and simpler in two ways: one, the migrating hunter-gatherers do not have to keep upgrading or changing their life skills dramatically, so their progress can be quick. Two, a coastal route gives an unintentional direction to their migration, taking them forward inexorably, unlike an inland route with its surprises, roundabouts and uncertainties.

Now to come back to our topic, the distance from, say, Yemen on the Arabian peninsula to Australia, if you take the coastal route, is not much more than the distance from Alaska to the southern tip of Argentina. So even if you assume it would take double the time, it is perhaps possible to cover the distance in about 4000 to 5000 years, assuming, of course, that migrants mostly take the coastal route as the first migrants to the Americas did. Now if you start with the middle point of 65,000 years ago for the Australian evidence of modern humans, then the walkathon from Africa should have begun about 70,000 years ago, which is still within the ballpark of the genetic estimates, though it would mean a crossing at the Red Sea into the Arabian peninsula during the glacial period.[8]

---

[8] The crucial assumption here is that the migrants are beachcombers, surviving mainly by their skills in using marine resources. Is this a realistic assumption? Archaeology says it's possible. From around 125,000 years ago in Africa, we begin to see evidence of modern humans being beachcombers, surviving by catching fish and shells. The proof is usually easy to spot: piles and piles of split shells (called shell middens). The earliest evidence of shell middens comes from the Abdur site on the Eritrean coast, just across the Red Sea from the Arabian peninsula. The site also yielded remains of large mammals, suggesting that though these modern humans were into seafood, they were not exclusively so. There have been other early finds of shell middens in Africa – such as from the Klasies river mouth in South Africa. But the Abdur find caused a frisson of excitement because it was so close to the Southern Route.

Modern humans, usually terrestrial hunter-gatherers, may have turned to marine resources during one of the glacial periods, when aridity and cold turned large parts of Africa into deserts. But sea levels would have been much lower during these

What does genetics say about all this? Is it in line with the idea of a rapid dispersal of beachcombing modern humans out of Africa using the Southern Route and reaching Australia from Yemen in about 5000 years or so? The answer is an emphatic yes. Genetic evidence is not just compatible with such a quick expansion, it actually demands such a rapid spread. The reason is that if the spread was slow with many rests in between, the genetic tree would look 'nested', and that is not the case. To take a theoretical example, if haplogroup M spread to India and settled there for a few thousand years, then a few subhaplogroups of M would have emerged because of mutations, and therefore the next migration out of India to, say, Myanmar would have included those subhaplogroups. If those subhaplogroups then spent a few thousand years in Myanmar before moving on to, say, Thailand, we would have seen many more new subhaplogroups emerging and taking part in the migration to the next destination. Thus, successive regions would have received successive subhaplogroups. If you drew the phylogenetic tree of such an expansion, it would look like one subhaplogroup nested under another, and then under another and so on, as we move from one region to another. But what we see in reality is nothing like that. M spread all the way to Australia, before too many mutations could arise. And each region has its own direct subhaplogroups of M. In short, genetics strongly supports a rapid expansion to Australia after the African exodus.

If such a rapid migration peopled Asia roughly between 70,000 and 60,000 years ago, there aren't enough modern human fossils from this period in south Asia to confirm it. The fossils that we do have from the region are of a much younger age. The earliest modern human fossil in south Asia was found in Sri Lanka, at the Fa Hien caves in the Kalutara district, dated to about 35,000 years ago. More modern human fossil finds from the Batadombalena caves, also in Sri Lanka,

cold periods than they are now, and most of the sites with evidence of their coastal settlements would now be underwater.

are dated to about 28,000 years ago. These discoveries proved beyond doubt that the migrants from Africa would have been quite at home in coastal India, and even in the tropical island of Sri Lanka. Fossils in both these places were found along with Microlithic (or tiny stone) tools that might have been used to give sharp tips to arrows and spears. Such Microlithic tools are typically associated with modern humans as opposed to archaic or extinct members of the *Homo* species.

But if the first modern humans travelled down the western coast of India, and then up the eastern coast, before moving to south-east Asia and then to China and Japan as well as Australia, why have there been no fossil or shell midden or even stone tool findings along the Indian coast? One reason could be that the period between 71,000 and 57,000 years ago was a glacial period (MIS 4), and sea levels would have been lower than they are today. So the first migrants would have been moving through regions that are all below the sea today, thus reducing our chances of finding proof along the coast. Proof would become available only when people moved inland, such as in Fa Hien, and that might have taken time and, therefore, the earliest evidence of modern human presence in south Asia is likely to be of a much younger age than the date of the first migration itself.

Not all archaeologists or geneticists buy into the coastal migration route, though. Ravi Korisettar of Karnatak University and the geneticist Stephen Oppenheimer and the archaeologist Michael Haslam of the University of Oxford recently argued in a paper[9] that the slope of the coast would determine how much of the continental shelf became visible when the sea level retreated. A continental shelf with a very low slope would reveal a lot of new land, perhaps tens of kilometres wide, while a continental shelf with a steep slope would reveal little new land. According to these scientists, the Indian continental shelf,

---

[9] Ravi Korisettar, et al., 'Out of Africa, into South Asia: A Review of Archaeological and Genetic Evidence for the Dispersal of *Homo sapiens* into the Indian Subcontinent', in *Beyond Stones and More Stones*, Ravi Korisettar, ed. (The Mythic Society, 2017).

especially on the western coast, mostly has a steep slope, and so it is unlikely that the First Indians were walking along lands that later went under the sea. The reason why we have not found evidence of the coastal migration route, they say, is that modern humans were opportunistic in the routes they took, sometimes taking the coastal route and sometimes the inland routes. These are arguments that will be settled only when we find older modern human fossils.

Now that we have dated the first modern human settlers in India to sometime around 65,000 years ago (because they had to have left Africa about 70,000 years ago based on Australian and south-east Asian fossil finds as we discussed earlier), let us tackle some outstanding questions about how the rest of the world was populated before moving ahead with our story. We have so far talked about OoA migrants moving through the Arabian peninsula into south Asia and then going on to populate east Asia and Australia. But what about Europe and central Asia? When did those regions get populated? The earliest evidence for modern human occupation of Europe dates to about 45,000 years ago (the irony of this shouldn't be missed: when the first migrants, or the aborigines, reached Australia around 65,000 years ago, the Europeans did not exist).

This delay in populating Europe – a gap of about 25,000 years between the OoA episode and the first evidence of modern humans in Europe – suggests that the route from the Arabian peninsula to Europe was not open until the climate warmed up quite a bit. There would have been two major obstacles on the route from the Arabian peninsula into Europe during the glacial period. One, the Rub' al Khali or 'Empty Quarter', the largest contiguous sand desert in the world which occupies the southern third of the Arabian peninsula, and two, the Zagros and Taurus mountains of Iran, which would have been an equally formidable barrier. So the place that the first migrants went to occupy after south Asia was probably not Europe, but central Asia, conclude Korisettar and the other scientists in the paper mentioned above. They possibly walked from where Pakistan is today, up the Indus banks and into central Asia. And then, after the climate got warmer around 57,000 years ago, some of the people from the OoA migration still living in the Arabian peninsula or somewhere close to south Asia could have moved west across the Zagros mountains into Turkey, Syria, Israel and Europe. That might have been followed later by a second migration from central Asia to Europe around 30,000 years ago.

Around the same time as some of the central Asian groups were moving into Europe, others might have migrated to the regions around Beringia, which would function as a land bridge between Alaska and Siberia during extreme cold climate, and which would have served as the staging ground for the first migrants into the Americas around 16,000 years ago. Before this migration to the Americas from Asia, some of the early occupants of east Asia had moved into Siberia and the regions around it like Beringia and mixed with the people there. Thus, the migrants moving into the Americas would have had an east Asian genetic heritage as well, not just a central Asian one. So that completes a very skeletal history of OoA and the subsequent migrations that filled up the world.

The southern petal of Jambudvipa

The cosmology of most cultures portrays the place they inhabit as the centre of the universe. Our own cosmology, common to Buddhism, Hinduism and Jainism, is similar but only in some ways. (This cosmology was probably brought in or created by one of the later migrants into south Asia, but let us keep that aside for the moment.) In the telling of that cosmology, it is our world, called Jambudvipa, that lies at the centre of seven concentric circles of alternating land and sea. The sea is made up, successively from inward to outward, of salt water, sugarcane juice, wine, ghee, curd, milk and water. And at the raised centre of Jambudvipa rises Meru, the mountain, the abode of the gods. In some visualizations, Jambudvipa is divided into four vast regions, each one shaped like the four petals of a lotus, with Meru at the centre, like a pericarp, the southern petal being Bharatvarsha.

When the first group of modern humans walked into India, perhaps no more than a few hundred people in groups of twenty or twenty-five, trekking all the way from the Arabian peninsula over hundreds of years or perhaps even a thousand or more years, did they have a cosmology of their own that tried to explain the inexplicable? And did they have any inkling that they were entering a special place that more than a billion of their descendants would one day call their home? We are unlikely to ever know the answers to such questions, but there are other questions that we can crack with the technology and material evidence that we have. Questions such as: when they entered India, were they walking into a country that they had all to themselves – like the first modern humans in Australia or the Americas – or did they have competition in the form of other members of the *Homo* species, like in the Levant and Arabia? Did they tangle with each other? Or did they tango? Did our ancestors drive the others to extinction? Did they bring advanced technology – like bows and arrows and spears – or did they come with just a Middle Palaeolithic stone toolkit of scrapers, axes and sharp flakes that could be used as blades? And, of course, what did they look like? Do we have their direct descendants among us today? How big a brood have they left behind? Where can we find them?

Let us start with the most tangible question first. What did they look like? We know that the Onge in the Andaman Islands are descendants of the original OoA migrants who may have mixed less with other groups. But does that mean the First Indians looked like them? That would be stretching things too far.

Today's Onge are as distant chronologically from the first migrants as any of us. This is such an obvious truth that it shouldn't be necessary to say it. But it is surprising how often our mind plays tricks with us. For example, when we think of the earliest modern humans, say, those who existed 300,000 years ago, our mental picture of them

A member of the Onge tribe on India's Little Andaman Island

may resemble today's Africans. But this is an ill-conceived idea. The Africans of today are exactly as removed from the earliest modern humans as we are, and have gone through similar levels of mutation and change as the rest of humanity. They are no closer to the early modern humans than we are. Mutations can change the colour of the skin, the shape of the nose, the texture of the hair, or the slant of the eye – not to speak of such things as the ability to survive at high altitudes (Tibetans) or to stay underwater for long (the Bajau people of Southeast Asia).

Similarly, in the case of the Onge too, 60,000 or 65,000 years is a long time for mutations to have done their work, and also for drift and selection pressures to have winnowed the genetic field. What is drift and selection? Genetic drift is the phrase geneticists use to describe the tendency of small sequestered populations to have declining genetic diversity over time. The principle is simple. In every generation, there is a chance that the last person carrying a particular genetic variation may die without leaving an heir. In a large population, the chances of any single genetic variation dwindling down to having just one last representative is low and, therefore, the effect of drift will be less too. In other words, small populations are likely to lose enough diversity over time and become more homogeneous – or rather, drift towards a uniform genetic standard. So in a given time, drift alone could make a small population look very different from how they used to look.

The word 'selection', on the other hand, alludes to the essential process of evolution – the physical environment or the social environment or sexual preferences lending greater genetic success to some traits or mutations and less success to others, thus shaping the evolution of a population in a particular way. So it is highly likely that because of all these – mutations, drift and selection – the Onge today look quite different from what the First Indians looked like. (This is precisely the process – mutation, drift and selection – that makes different population groups separated by distance or other geographical barriers grow genetically distinct over time.)

Until we find a well-preserved skeleton from some 65,000 years ago that we can use to reconstruct the faces of the first migrants, we have only one other, suboptimal, option: look for ancient skeletons of modern humans from other regions. And we do have one from the Skhul cave of Israel, although it is dated much earlier, between 80,000 and 120,000 years ago. It is the skeleton of a female modern human, and the reconstructed face shows a person we can easily identify with, but with some distinct differences. (Search for an image of 'mitochondrial eve' on the net.) Of course, we have no idea what level of difference existed among modern humans in different parts of Africa and the Levant over 80,000 years ago. It is possible that the people who moved into the Arabian peninsula (who would eventually reach south Asia) looked quite different from those who broke into the Levant. But this is the best we can do as of now.

An equally important question, which has implications for the way modern humans settled in different parts of the subcontinent, is this:

when they walked into India, did they run smack into archaic members of the *Homo* species already settled here? Without doubt, yes. This does not mean we have lots of fossil evidence to prove the existence of archaic or extinct members of the *Homo* species in the subcontinent when the modern humans arrived; we have almost none. (The only archaic human fossil evidence we have is a cranium discovered at Hathnora on the Narmada riverbank dated to around 250,000 years ago, which we will discuss in chapter 2.) What we do have, instead, are lots and lots of stone tools belonging to different styles and ages – from the Lower Palaeolithic to the Middle Palaeolithic and Microlithic – making it clear that India was by no means an inviting, empty land when our ancestors arrived.

Palaeolithic just means old stones, and Microlithic means tiny stones. Lower Palaeolithic covers the oldest-style stone tools created by modern and archaic humans – essentially choppers, cleavers and axes, all of them big and heavy and made by chipping away at large stones, often in a style called Acheulian. In Middle Palaeolithic, the style of the tools changes, with humans learning how to prepare a 'core' from a big stone in such a way that many, many different flakes can be struck off to make scrapers and points and so on, thus reducing the time and effort needed to make tools and also improving their quality.[10]

Middle Palaeolithic tools are smaller in comparison to Lower Palaeolithic tools, and Microlithic tools are smaller still, with some measuring less than a centimetre. These were often blades or points or variations of them and were often attached to bones or sticks and used as knives or arrows or spear tips.

---

[10] In the Acheulian style of toolmaking, a fist-sized or larger-sized stone is worked on, usually with another stone, to knock off several flakes and create a core with a jagged edge that can then be used as a tool for hacking, pounding or cutting. Acheulian tools are often called 'bifaces', meaning they have been worked symmetrically on both sides. Here, the core itself is the tool and the flakes are the discarded waste. In the Middle Palaeolithic style of toolmaking, first a core is prepared in such a manner that multiple flakes with sharp edges can be struck off easily from it. In this case, it is these flakes which are then used as tools, while the core from which all the flakes were made is ultimately discarded.

Microlithic tools are closely associated with modern humans, but not so the Palaeolithic or Middle Palaeolithic tools. Any modern or archaic human could have made them and so just by looking at these tools we cannot say with certainty which member of the *Homo* species was responsible for them. In other words, through much of their history, modern humans and archaic humans made much the same kinds of tools, though there could have been some regional variations. Broadly, the categorization of tools as Lower and Middle Palaeolithic or Microlithic refers to their type, not their age.

The earliest evidence of Palaeolithic tools in India is from Attirampakkam in Tamil Nadu, sixty-nine kilometres from Chennai, and dated to around 1.5 million years ago (that is, 1.2 million years before modern humans emerged). The Hunsgi–Baichbal valley in northern Karnataka (around 1.2 million years ago), the Middle Son valley in Madhya Pradesh, the Shivalik Hills in the outer Himalaya – the subcontinent is littered with evidence of the widespread presence of archaic humans much before modern humans set foot in the region or even evolved. Did all of them belong to the same species as the Narmada discovery, perhaps *Homo heidelbergensis* or *Homo erectus*? Or were there Neanderthals as well? Or another archaic human, as yet undiscovered? That is not entirely unlikely. We may not have yet identified all the varieties of archaic humans – not even those that were contemporaneous with our own ancestors when they were spreading around the world.

The Denisovans, for example, were discovered only about a decade ago when an ancient juvenile finger bone and a few teeth were retrieved from the Denisova caves in the Altai mountains of southern Siberia and the finger bone was later DNA sequenced. The DNA analysis made it clear, to everyone's surprise, that this was a species quite different from both modern humans and Neanderthals. The fossil assemblage was dated to between 50,000 and 30,000 years ago. Until this discovery, there was never any suggestion that such a species existed; in fact, the Denisovans are yet to be given a proper species name.

So, in short, we know south Asia had abundant presence of archaic humans but we do not know precisely who they were. We know, though, that they were smart enough to be among the first in the world to upgrade their tool technology from the traditional to the state of the art. At Attirampakkam, we have evidence that they moved up from making Lower Palaeolithic tools to Middle Palaeolithic tools around 385,000 years ago. This came to light only because of the outstanding and long-term work of the archaeologist Shanti Pappu and her team at Attirampakkam, and their findings about the emergence of Middle Palaeolithic tools in this region around 385,000 years ago were published as late as in January 2018.

The transition from Lower to Middle Palaeolithic toolmaking was a huge conceptual jump. This is because to start making Middle-Palaeolithic-style tools, you need to think many, many steps ahead, keeping in mind the final shape of the tool you want, and then shaping the core in such a manner that you can knock off precisely the kind of sharp tools you want, with very few strokes. If a Middle Palaeolithic toolmaker wanted to put down an Acheulian-style toolmaker, he could honestly say: any idiot can do that. (Any idiot doesn't include us, of course, because stone knapping is a specialized skill today, and we would need a lot of practice to become an expert knapper.)

Up against our cousins

We know from the history of early human expansion into the Levant that modern humans found it difficult to break into regions where archaic humans were already dominant. So it is reasonable to assume that when our ancestors arrived at the threshold of India, they too found themselves stymied, as in the Levant. In the paper mentioned earlier, Korisettar, Oppenheimer and Haslam suggest a new model for how modern humans may have responded to the situation, terming it the 'Indian staged dispersal'. In broad-brush terms this means our ancestors arrived at different parts of the subcontinent at different times, and did not expand all over it in one fell sweep. They are all from the same, single OoA migration, but they may have reached different regions of India at different times, just as they reached different parts of the world at different times.

The opening assumption of the scientists is that archaic humans would have been present in far more intimidating numbers in peninsular India than in northern India. A valid observation, as evidenced by the archaeological discoveries in Attirampakkam, Hunsgi–Baichbal valley, Middle Son valley, Bhimbetka, etc., all south of the Vindhyas. So the incoming modern humans would have taken a sub-Himalayan route across the subcontinent, the scientists posit, avoiding the peninsular region, and going on to Myanmar and then south-east Asia and further on to Australia, east Asia and China. There is, of course, no reason why all the First Indians need have taken only the sub-Himalayan route. Some of them could have taken a coastal route that would have kept them out of the way of the troublesome archaic humans who were present in the central and interior parts of the peninsula. We know today that that was what happened when the first migrants arrived in the Americas – they took different routes and got separated for thousands of years. Either way, the First Indians may have managed to avoid a direct and immediate conflict with the existing robust populations of archaic humans. When we talk about migrants having taken this or that route or having gone here or there, it is not to suggest they would have en masse vacated the areas they were occupying to go and settle in new regions. It means that they and their descendants kept expanding their range into newer and newer areas, without necessarily vacating the places they were already in.

Over time, the modern humans would have expanded their footprint in the subcontinent, even moving south and displacing the archaic humans and probably driving them to extinction. The sudden appearance of Microlithic tools in the Indian archaeological record may be a clue to when and how this may have happened. Even though stone tools don't necessarily help us identify different species of humans most of the time, microliths are a kind of exception. In India and elsewhere, they have been linked more closely with modern humans than archaic humans, and in the subcontinent we see microliths making their appearance around 45,000 years ago. Thereafter, they show a surprising level of continuity and expansion, and not just in the subcontinent. We see a similar emergence of microliths in Sri Lanka around 38,000 years ago, and they persist from then on till approximately 3000 years ago, nearabout when iron makes its presence felt, both in India and in Sri Lanka.

The earliest microliths in South Asia were found at Mehtakheri in Madhya Pradesh, dated to 45,000 years ago. Mehtakheri is one of eight sites in the Nimar region of Madhya Pradesh that had microliths ranging in age from 45,000 years to 3400 years. Curiously, the timing and location of the early finds of microliths tally quite nicely with the timing and location of an expansion (increase in population) of some First Indian lineages. According to the 2017 paper on the genetic chronology of the Indian subcontinent mentioned earlier, there was a major expansion and dispersal of mtDNA haplogroup M in central and eastern India between 45,000 and 35,000 years ago.[11] Towards the end of this period is also when the climate slowly began to deteriorate as the world got closer to the full glacial conditions of MIS 2.

So there are many things happening together: the climate slowly starts getting more dry and arid, putting stress on all living populations; modern humans start relying more and more on Microlithic tools; and their population then starts expanding and spreading to new areas. The region where all of this takes place, central India, also happens to be one of the most favoured areas for archaic humans to inhabit.

---

[11] Marina Silva, et al., 'A Genetic Chronology for the Indian Subcontinent Points to Heavily Sex-biased Dispersals', *BMC Evolutionary Biology* (2017).

Could it be that as modern humans in India found their habitats becoming drier and more arid, they responded by depending more and more on a new technology that involved making microliths and using them to create weapons like spears and arrows in order to hunt better and beat rival claimants to food and other resources? And could they have then moved into new areas that were still habitable but that they had hitherto avoided because of the presence of archaic humans there? If that is what they had indeed done, it could be said that they succeeded in all their missions, which resulted in a rapid rise in their population.

A 2009 study, 'Population Increase and Environmental Deterioration Correspond with Microlithic Innovations in South Asia ca. 35,000 Years Ago',[12] authored by some of the biggest names in archaeology and genetics, says, 'It has been estimated that between about 45,000 and 20,000 years ago, most of humanity lived in South Asia. This evidence is thought to reflect a population expansion in the subcontinent that is unparalleled elsewhere.'

Like the archaic humans in Attirampakkam who were at the cutting edge of technology around 385,000 years ago when they moved up to making Middle Palaeolithic tools, the modern humans of central India can lay claim to having been at the forefront of technology once again around 45,000 yeas ago, as they started making and using Microlithic tools and weapons. However, while the earliest microliths at Mehtakheri are dated to about 45,000 years ago, the technology would have arrived in different regions on the subcontinent at different periods of time. In fact, it arrives only around 35,000 years ago at critical places such as Patne in Maharashtra, Jwalapuram in Andhra Pradesh and Fa Hien and Batadombalena in Sri Lanka.

So here is a scenario that we can put together, based on what we know: around 65,000 years ago, modern humans arrive in India and are blindsided by the presence of archaic humans who have been well

---

[12] Michael Petraglia, et al., 'Population Increase and Environmental Deterioration Correspond with Microlithic Innovations in South Asia ca. 35,000 Years Ago', *PNAS* (July 2009).

settled in the region for hundreds of thousands of years. They then move in a gradual and opportunistic manner, some going across sub-Himalayan northern India from the west to the east, and some taking the coastal route from the north to the south. By the time the climate reached crisis point around 35,000 years ago, modern humans had already equipped themselves with better technology to hunt down their prey and beat back their rivals. As success built on success, the rapidly growing population of modern humans started expanding their range and moving deeper into the peninsular region, thus probably forcing archaic humans to restrict themselves to local refuges – such as Jwalapuram or perhaps Bhimbetka – until they went extinct.

Jwalapuram is a good place to understand how this might have worked. Located in the Jurreru river valley of Kurnool district, its significance lies in the fact that the river basin holds layers of ash left behind by the Toba supervolcanic eruption of 74,000 years ago. When the volcano erupted in the Sumatran island, millions of tonnes of ash was dumped all over south-east Asia and south Asia, causing stress to all life in the region.

The Jwalapuram site was discovered by Professor Korisettar and was excavated a decade ago by a team of archaeologists led by him and Professor Petraglia. They found something remarkable at the bottom-most layer, under the ash: Middle Palaeolithic tools dated to around 77,000 years ago, made by who they thought were modern humans. They also found a continuation of the same tool technology above the ash layer, but dated to 45,000 to 35,000 years ago. Those findings created a stir because these frontally challenged the version that said OoA happened only around 70,000 years ago. Petraglia holds on to the theory that these tools were made by modern humans but the paper co-authored by Korisettar, Oppenheimer and Haslam in 2017 says that these products are 'most likely the product of archaic hominins'.

More interestingly, Korisettar and Petraglia also found microliths appearing in the same Jurreru valley, starting from around 38,000 years ago and persisting until a few thousand years ago. Regarding these microliths, Korisettar, Oppenheimer and Haslam say, 'we see the most parsimonious explanation for the Jurreru material record to be the movement of modern humans into the area 40,000 to 35,000 years ago'.

If this interpretation is correct, that the Jurreru valley was a settlement of archaic humans where *Homo sapiens* came around 35,000 to 40,000 years ago, then the valley could have been one of the most prominent sites in the conflict between modern humans – armed with the new technology of microliths – and their archaic cousins – still working with Middle Palaeolithic tools. Whether it was also one of the last, we will probably never know.

As you approach the wide open terrain of Jwalapuram you can see people carting away the Toba volcanic ash in sacks, to be sold as detergent or brass polish. When I visited the site in early 2018, there were trenches dug by miners, and a few metres down their walls wide bands of white ash, the remains of the mega eruption, could be clearly seen. When the volcano erupted, only about five centimetres of ash had fallen on the valley, but the band you see today is inches, not just centimetres, thick. This is because apart from the primary ash fall, the valley, for a long time afterwards, had been receiving more ash carried into it by monsoon rains, streams and the Jurreru river.

As you stand on the riverbed, it is tantalizing to try to visualize the drama that might have unfolded about 38,000 years ago on this ground, as the first modern humans of India moved into what could have been one of the last remaining refuges of archaic humans. How long did it take for the modern humans to complete the occupation of India and when did the last archaic humans on this land pass into history? Those are secrets that science is yet to unravel, but by looking at how far they were able to reach into South Asia (all the way across to south-west Sri Lanka by about 38,000 years ago) and to what extent they were able to move into the long-standing preserves of our archaic cousins (Jwalapuram by about 35,000 years ago), we can fairly assume that by around that time our ancestors were truly masters of the land they came into some 30,000 years earlier.

For a glimpse of the First Indians, look in the mirror!

This leads us to the next questions: where are their descendants today? How many are there, and where can we find them? If you want to find their closest direct descendants living today, who haven't mixed with other populations all that much, you need to go to the Little Andaman Island and look up the Onge. There are only about a hundred of them left now, down from about 670 in 1900. Their maternal haplogroup is M and paternal haplogroup is D. They made it to the news in 2011 when a new baby was born, taking the strength of the tribe to 101.

But really, if you want to see the lineage of the First Indians, you probably only need to look into the mirror or look around in your office or home. Unlike many other regions – such as Europe, Australia or the Americas – which have seen the lineage of their original inhabitants dwindle to very low levels, the genetic lineage of the First Indians forms the foundation, the bedrock, of the Indian population today.

In fact, between half and two-thirds of our genome-wide ancestry today comes from the First Indians. This genome-wide figure, which applies to both men and women, is the most appropriate measure to grasp the genetic make-up of Indians, but there are other ways to look at it too, which provide other kinds of insights. For example, if you look at mtDNA lineages you will find that somewhere between 70 and 90 per cent of people are descendants of the First Indians, with M lineages being the most popular. If you look at Y-chromosome lineages, though, the picture is different: First Indian descendants account for only 10 to 40 per cent of the haplogroups, depending on which population group you are considering. (This massive difference between the male and female lines of descent encapsulates the history of later migrations, which we will tackle in chapter 4.)

At this point you could refer back to pp. 19–26 that dealt with mtDNA and Y-chromosome lineages, or here is a brief summary. MtDNA is transferred from mother to daughter in an unbroken chain, while Y-chromosome is transferred from father to son similarly. So when we say that somewhere between 70 and 90 per cent of mtDNA lineages derive their origin from the First Indians, it means that in the case of 70 to 90 per cent of Indian women, if you traced their maternal line back through the ages, you will arrive at a woman who was an original OoA migrant and reached India some 65,000 years ago. Similarly, when we say that 10 to 40 per cent of Y-chromosome lineages are of

Subhendu Sarkar / LightRocket / Getty Images

A woman belonging to the Bonda tribe in Koraput, Odisha.
The Bonda speak Remo, an Austroasiatic language.

A woman belonging to the Gond tribe in Bastar, Chhattisgarh.
The Gond speak Gondi, a Dravidian language.

Joerg Boethling / Alamy Stock Photo

First Indian descent, it means that in the case of 10 to 40 per cent of all Indian men, if you traced their paternal line back through the ages, you will arrive at a man who was an original OoA migrant.

So here is a question: if you were to identify a single person who embodies us Indians the best, who do you think it should be? Ideally, it should be a tribal woman because she is most likely to be carrying the deepest-rooted and widest-spread mtDNA lineage in India today, M2. In a genetic sense, she would represent all of our history, with very little left out. She shares the most with the largest number of Indians, no matter where in the social ladder they stand, what language they speak and which region they inhabit because we are all migrants, and we are all mixed. And she was here from the beginning. And she was most likely also at Mohenjo-daro as the 'dancing girl' (the image on the cover) about 4500 years ago, during the period that most shaped us as we are today.

But before we get to the urban civilization of Mohenjo-daro, Harappa, Dholavira, Rakhigarhi and the other cities and towns in the valleys of the Indus and Ghaggar–Hakra twin river systems, we need to know how we became farmers from hunter-gatherers, over what period of time and why.

2

The First Farmers

How the First Indians and Zagrosian herders from Iran planted the first seeds of an agricultural revolution that spread like wildfire across India's north-western region, creating the necessary conditions for the birth of the world's largest early civilization.

One way to understand the population structure of today's India is to think of it as a pizza, with the First Indians forming its base. Some parts of the pizza are thin crust, some parts thick crust, but all parts need to have the base – the pizza doesn't exist without it. Then comes the sauce that is spread all over the pizza. And then the cheese and the toppings – the people who came into the subcontinent later, at various periods. The cheese and the toppings are not uniform across the different slices. Some slices have an extra topping of tomato, some have more of capsicum and others a lot of mushroom. The sauce, the cheese or the toppings that you find on this Indian pizza are not unique; these are found in other parts of the world too – some in West Asia, some in Southeast Asia and some in Europe and central Asia. But the base of the pizza is unique to India – you will not find another one like it anywhere else in the world. And neither will you find a pizza with this level of diversity in any place other than Africa.

What accounts for this level of diversity, this distinction, of India? In a sense, this is the story of this book. A large part of the genetic diversity is due to South Asia perhaps being second only to Africa in having been occupied for the longest time by a large population of modern humans. This itself generates diversity because with each generation and each replication of an individual's genome, mutations can occur and over time these differences accumulate. And the larger the population, the larger the number of new mutations. As we saw in the last chapter, India has had one of the largest modern human populations in the world for tens of thousands of years. But that is only part of the reason for the diversity. The other major reason is migrations.

So let us try to understand how we ended up where we are today from the ground up. This chapter will look at the first major migration that reshaped India's demography after the First Indians reached the subcontinent some 65,000 years ago.

Masters of all they see

When we left the previous chapter, the First Indians had finally become masters of the land they had migrated to, having driven the archaic humans to extinction. Or at least having outlasted them. When exactly did the archaic humans in India go extinct? We have no real, fact-based understanding of this. In fact, we do not even know for sure what species they belonged to – *Homo erectus*, *Homo heidelbergensis*, *Homo neanderthalensis* or a species that is yet to be identified.

There has only been one discovery of an archaic human fossil in South Asia – a partially complete cranium dated to around 250,000 years ago, recovered from Hathnora in Madhya Pradesh's Narmada valley in 1982. It was first classified as a *Homo erectus*, then as an 'archaic' version of *Homo sapiens* itself, then as *Homo heidelbergensis*, and as of now the debate is still unsettled. It is not surprising then that we do not know when these archaic humans went extinct in the subcontinent either.

We do know, though, that Neanderthals went extinct in Europe around 40,000 years ago, with the Iberian peninsula in south-western Europe being their last stand and refuge. Modern humans reached Europe around 45,000 years ago, so they had a few thousand years of coexistence with Neanderthals. The nature of modern human interaction with Neanderthals in Europe is a matter of debate, but it is safe to say that soon after modern humans reached the continent, Neanderthals had to retreat from everywhere because of conflict with the new arrivals or because of new diseases spread by them or because of a number of other factors.

In India the extinction of the archaic *Homo* species may have happened around 35,000 years ago, as we saw in chapter 1, and *Homo sapiens* would have then become for the first time master of all they surveyed. So modern humans in India have had a very long time to spread themselves out and make their presence felt all over the habitable regions of the subcontinent in the north, east, south and west. This explains why the 'Indian pizza' has a base that is present throughout South Asia.

But why is this base unique? It is unique because the ancestry of the First Indians forms the base, or 50 to 65 per cent of the ancestry of Indian population groups. And this First Indian ancestry has no close relatives outside the subcontinent today. Its closest relatives once left India to migrate to south-east Asia and then the rest of east Asia and Australia, but that separation happened around 65,000 years ago and it would be a stretch to call any of them close relatives any more – deep time makes separated populations evolve differently along different paths. That is why the base of the Indian pizza is both unique and omnipresent in the region – almost all regions, all linguistic groups and all castes and tribes of the country carry the genetic imprint of the First Indians, as scientific studies have shown repeatedly. This is also why it is accurate to describe them as the foundation or the base of the Indian population.

Why then is the base thin in some regions, such as the north-west, and thick in some other regions, such as the south? This can be put down to subsequent migrations into India from the outside which, to varying degrees, replaced, displaced or subsumed the First Indians. Broadly, areas such as the north-west or the north-east, the regions through which newer migrants arrived, have a thinner base of First Indians than central or peninsular India.

Who are these later migrants and when did they arrive? To answer this, we need to turn to palaeoclimate, or the climate during ancient times. As we saw earlier, the earliest evidence for microliths in the subcontinent dates to about 45,000 years ago, and by 35,000 years ago or so they had become widespread. The climate had already started deteriorating as the world began its descent towards a long glacial period that would last from around 29,000 years ago to 14,000 years ago. But the ending of the glacial age wasn't quite neat and dramatic: the gradual warming that began near the end of the glacial age was interrupted by another cold twitch that lasted about 1300 years, between 12,900 and 11,700 years ago, when the world climate turned dry and arid once more, during the phase called Younger Dryas. It is only when the Younger Dryas too ended that the world really entered a long-lasting warm, wetter and greener period called Holocene 11,700 years ago. We are still in the Holocene.

It is often during periods of climatic upheaval such as these that we see new dramatic developments taking place in human history, proving once again that our species needs either fear (lack of resources) or greed (promise of plenty) to propel it forward. For example, around 16,000 years ago when the glacial period was slowly coming to an end, the Americas were being occupied for the first time by Asians coming in through Beringia, the land bridge that connected the two continents where modern-day Russia and Alaska are.

Thus in the early Holocene we see on–off experiments in the Fertile

Crescent in west Asia (today's Iraq, Iran and the Levant), south Asia, Egypt and later China. These experiments would ultimately lead to humankind taking to agriculture almost everywhere. Not all these experiments were successful; not all those successful were sustainable; and many experiments that did not succeed or sustain for long may not be traceable in the archaeological records today. But when agriculture finally took off for certain in the Fertile Crescent and in India, Egypt and China over a transitionary period of 4000 or 5000 years between 9700 BCE and 5000 BCE, the human population started exploding in a manner never seen before, leading to massive migrations that changed world demography in Europe, central Asia, south Asia, China and east Asia.

Miracle in Mehrgarh

The hotspot of the earliest experiments in agriculture in south Asia is a village today called Mehrgarh, located at the foot of the Bolan Pass in Balochistan in modern-day Pakistan. The site was inhabited for a period of about 4400 years between, roughly, 7000 BCE and 2600 BCE. At its peak, it covered an area of about 200 hectares, which would make it one of the largest habitations of the period between the Indus and the Mediterranean.

Mehrgarh was discovered as a historical site in 1976 by a French archaeological mission working in collaboration with Pakistan's department of archaeology, and it dramatically changed our understanding of how agriculture began and spread in south Asia. Mehrgarh laid the foundations for the Harappan Civilization that was to follow. The excavated mound at Mehrgarh had cultural deposits (material remains that had been used, made or changed by humans) that were nine metres thick, covering the period from around 7000 BCE. When people live in a settlement for hundreds or thousands of years, the accumulated refuse and debris – especially bricks – cause the ground level to rise, forming mounds. The thickness of the deposits,

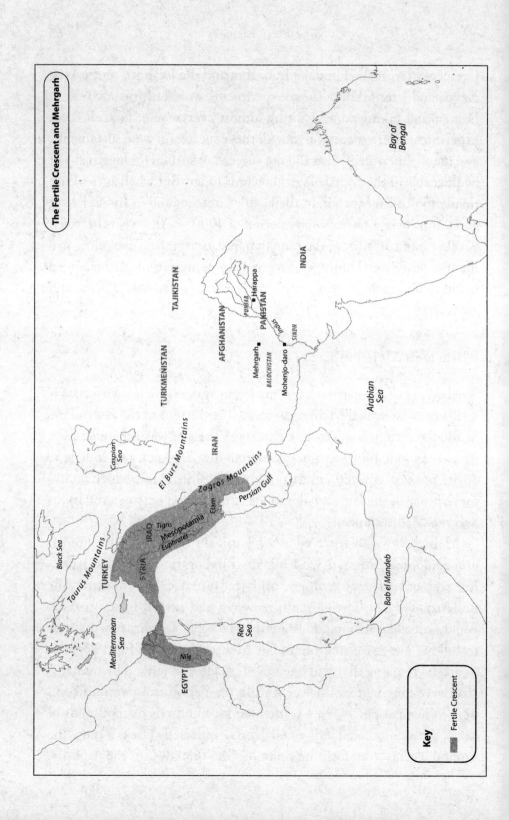

The Fertile Crescent and Mehrgarh

therefore, can be a rough indication of how long a settlement was occupied, in comparison with other sites in similar circumstances.

At the bottom-most layer the researchers found small, rectangular, multiroomed mud-brick houses, some of which may have been used for storage; sickles made of microliths attached originally to wooden handles that may have been used for harvesting grains; remains of barley and wheat grains in the soil and in the mud bricks; remains of meals, suggesting consumption of hunted animals such as gazelle, nilgai, blackbuck, wild pig and water buffalo; and evidence of domestication of the local humped cattle, zebu (*Bos indicus*), and perhaps goat as well.

Jean-François Jarrige, the leader of the French team, described their finds at the earliest levels, which were 'aceramic', or without pottery, thus: 'All the excavated buildings are multi-roomed structures. Four different plan-types have been recorded: two-roomed, four-roomed, six-roomed and ten-roomed buildings. Most of the walls of these buildings are composed of two rows of hand-moulded mudbricks longitudinally arranged. These long and narrow bricks measured 62 x 12 x 8 cm with generally on their upper faces a herringbone pattern of impressions of the brickmakers' thumbs to provide a keying for the mudmortar in which they were set.'[1] (Mudmortar refers to a paste used to bind together building blocks – in this case, bricks. The brickmaker's thumb impressions create a non-smooth surface which helps the mortar to hold the building blocks together.) Elsewhere Jarrige describes the bricks as being 'cigar-shaped'. Jarrige's team noted that the six-roomed buildings revealed no fireplace or significant remains of domestic activities, unlike what was found in some of the other buildings, thus suggesting that these bigger structures were probably used as granaries or storage facilities.

'The walls of the clay houses were plastered inside and outside with a 2 cm thick clay mortar. There are evidences that the coatings of the

---

[1] Jean-François Jarrige, 'Mehrgarh Neolithic', *Pragdhara* 18 (2006).

external walls of several houses were coloured in red or even adorned with paintings. A portion of a collapsed wall from level 1 [the earliest level of excavation, dated to around 7000 BCE] was coloured in plain red ochre. In the upper levels, similar traces of red paint were found on several walls. Quite sizeable fragmentary impressions of external plaster fallen on the ground show red V-shaped motifs and in one case, a complex geometrical pattern of red lines and red and black dots. Some floors made of packed and rammed earth were also covered with red ochre. Some roofing fragments have also been discovered in the building debris. They consisted of fragments of chaff-tempered mud with several impressions of fibrous stems of reeds.'

Many rooms in the smaller buildings had traces of fireplaces, and in the open spaces between houses many circular firepits were discovered, their diameters ranging between forty and sixty centimetres and with a maximum depth of about forty-five centimetres. Interestingly, most firepits had heavily burnt, cracked pebbles and one had oval-shaped clay balls. Their use wasn't difficult to decipher, since in Balochistan bread is cooked on heated stones even today.

The plant assemblage of Mehrgarh (or the selection of plants that were being used by the residents, as revealed by the remains excavated from the site) was dominated by a particular variety of barley, the naked six-row barley (naked means hull-less, and six-row refers to the number of spikelets with grains on them). It accounted for more than 90 per cent of the recorded seeds and imprints on the site. But were the residents of Mehrgarh just gathering wild barley or were they actively cultivating it? There's a way to find out.

All domesticated plants and animals differ from their wild ancestors in fairly predictable ways, because of the selection pressures that domestication puts on their evolution over time. Many domesticated animals, for example, become smaller in size, show less aggression, develop smaller brains and lose the more extravagant horns. Also, sexual dimorphism – where the male and female sizes differ significantly – slowly disappears. It is easy to see why. On the one hand, humans select their animals for their ease of taming and lack of aggression, which reflects in such changes as a smaller head or horns, less visibly dangerous teeth and smaller brains. On the other hand, many of the usual selection pressures on animals are taken away because they no longer have to compete with other animals of their species either for food or for mates.

Domestication causes many changes in plants too. For example, their seeds no longer shatter when ripe, and they germinate far more easily and are larger. It is easy to see why this happens too. When humans harvest their crop, the seeds that are already shattered are lost and dispersed in the soil while those that are still on the stem are collected. Some of them are used for consumption, and the rest kept for sowing in the next period. This acts as a strong selection pressure for seeds that do not shatter immediately on ripening. To look at it from the other side, since plants that are domesticated no longer have to worry about spreading their seeds – a job that is now taken over by humans – the usual selection pressures that make seedpods self-shatter cease to operate. Similar pressures explain how domesticated seeds of plants are often larger and why they germinate more easily too.

Because of these differences, scientists while looking at ancient fossils of animals or plants can figure out whether these were domesticated or wild. This is important because even if a settlement has, say, sickles and evidence of granaries and of consumption of cereals, this need not mean that the people were agriculturists – they could merely have been hunter-gatherers harvesting wild crops rather than cultivating them. The presence of domesticated animals and plants, on the other hand, is a clear indication that the people are indeed agriculturists, not hunter-gatherers. In the case of the barley found at the earliest levels at Mehrgarh, the anthropologist and agricultural scientist Lorenzo Constantini found it to be 'cultivated but not perhaps fully domesticated', meaning that the process of domestication was still under way.

What about the animals? Were they domesticated too? The residents of Mehrgarh were avid hunters, but there is also evidence of animal domestication, at first limited to goat. A few graves at the earliest excavation levels for young women had up to five complete skeletons of kids or young goats placed around their legs in a semicircle. The presence of bones of relatively small subadult and adult animals in the trash deposits at the earliest excavation levels also suggests the domesticated status of goats, according to the archaeologist and zoologist R.H. Meadow, who was part of excavations at both Mehrgarh and Harappa. This is because while hunters usually target bigger animals in a herd to maximize their gains, herders are likely to cull younger males. So the size of the animals consumed as evidenced by the trash deposits is a signal of the domestication process as well.

Meadow also showed that during Period 1 at Mehrgarh (that is, from around 7000 BCE to around 6000 BCE), sheep and cattle came to increasingly dominate the animal remains of the settlement, as opposed to the remains of hunted animals such as nilgai and gazelles – another indication of domestication. By the end of Period 1, cattle bones accounted for over half of the animal remains, with the indigenous humped cattle zebu becoming the dominant presence. According to Meadow, the animals in Mehrgarh grew smaller in body size over time, as is expected when the domestication process is on.

In the middle of all this – domesticating plants and animals, building houses, hunting – the residents of Mehrgarh also found time to indulge their creative side. Archaeologists found remains of workshops of beadmakers, who were using calcite or steatite (both are types of mineral rocks) as raw material. Grave goods – or things that are buried along with the dead – gave an even clearer picture of craft production in Mehrgarh. These included ornaments made of seashells, lapis lazuli, turquoise, black steatite and many other such stones. Note that since Mehrgarh is nowhere near the sea, the seashells indicate long-range trading or exchange networks that probably reached up to the Makran coast of today's Pakistan. The ornaments were created with an unexpected level of sophistication, says Jarrige.

He describes a particularly striking burial thus: 'Exceptional grave deposits are dentalium [a kind of long, thin shell] headbands found on the heads of several females . . . In Burial 274, the headband was made of woven rows of small dentalium segments and closed by two straps used as a clasp. Each of them was ornamented with four perforated natural shells. Around the neck was a thin necklace made of shell beads and at the waist, a belt-like ornament was made up of cylindrical shell beads and one flattened polyhedral shell head. Hanging on the belt, an interlacing of numerous threaded dentalium beads was found in front of the pelvis of the individual.'

But there was an even more impressive discovery. At an excavation level dated to around 6000 BCE, the archaeologists found imprints of cotton thread inside the holes of copper beads discovered in one of the two graves there – the first evidence of the use of cotton anywhere in the world, and also the first evidence of the use of copper in the subcontinent.

The quantity and quality of beads and other ornaments kept rising over time, with some of the raw materials coming from faraway areas. The techniques were also improving, with the beadmakers, for example, figuring out how to transform black steatite into white steatite by a heating process.

If crafts were flourishing, so it seems were other occupations – some graveyards show the earliest evidence of dentistry in archaeological records anywhere. Eleven drilled molar crowns from nine individuals (four females, two males and three unidentified) have been recorded. One individual has three drilled teeth; another has the same tooth drilled twice. We do not know whether there were full-time 'dentists', or part-time dabblers in a new profession, but one guesses the new Neolithic eating habits were not great news for the teeth of the Mehrgarhians! ('Neolithic' is associated with the beginnings of farming and the domestication of animals and plants in general. In archaeological records, this period is often represented by polished stone tools and implements such as grinding stones and, sometimes, pottery. The Neolithic Age is preceded by the Palaeolithic Age and succeeded by the Chalcolithic or Copper Age.)

The ceramic period in Mehrgarh began only around 6000 BCE – more than a thousand years after the start of the settlement. Until then, the people of Mehrgarh made do with baskets coated with bitumen (a naturally occurring sticky, black hydrocarbon mixture) and stone vessels. When the first few samples of pottery appear in Mehrgarh around 6000 BCE, they are pretty crudely made potsherds. But crucially these pots were not wheel-made, but constructed by 'assembling pieces of clay', perhaps using bitumen to hold them together. This early pottery technique is called sequential slab construction and we will come across this again later.

During the ceramic period, the number and size of storage structures increase dramatically, indicating a rising population. There

The Metropolitan Museum of Art, New York

A vessel in the Mehrgarh style, 3000–2500 BCE

is increasing use of fine, lustrous red pottery, but grave goods are no longer a common practice, except for a few beads seen now and then. By 5300 BCE, the Chalcolithic period had begun, and the progress in material culture continued unabated, with innovation upon innovation: wheel-turned pottery, cotton cultivation, terracotta figurines, all leading up to the early Harappan phase of the civilization by 3000 BCE. ('Early Harappan' only refers to the time period. Mehrgarh is not considered a part of the Harappan Civilization.)

The Mehrgarh site was abandoned sometime between 2600 BCE and 2000 BCE in favour of the larger, fortified city of Nausharo about five miles away. Mehrgarh is likely to have spawned a number of

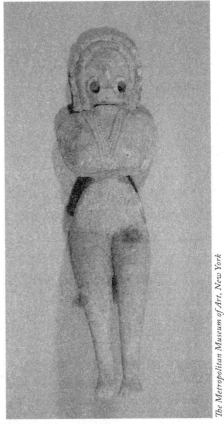

The Metropolitan Museum of Art, New York

Terracotta figurines of women in the Mehrgarh style, 3000–2500 BCE

Chalcolithic cultures in the region that were precursors to the full-
fledged Harappan Civilization, with names such Hakra, Kot Diji,
Amri, Nal and Ahar.

So within a period of about 5000 years, Mehrgarh had grown
from a small settlement beginning its experiments with farming to
perhaps an important centre[2] for the rapid expansion of a new way of
living across the north-western region of the subcontinent that would
ultimately lead to the making of the largest civilization of its time in
the valleys of the Indus and the Ghaggar–Hakra river. But who were
the people of Mehrgarh and where did they come from?

West Asian parallels

If you look back at the beginnings of Mehrgarh, you will notice that
there is a gap between the hunter-gatherer lifestyle that we saw in the
previous chapter and the lifestyle reflected in the excavation layers. It
is as if there's a missing link. The Mehrgarhians start building the first
mud-brick houses in the subcontinent and the first granaries as soon
as they set up base, and there is almost instant start-up of farming
and pastoralism, without the long lead times one observes in West
Asia, where the early experiments in agriculture began a few millennia
earlier, in fits and starts, often reaching dead ends and going no further,
as the changing climate sometimes spurred on new experimentation
and sometimes killed them off.

The story of agricultural beginnings in West Asia is not a linear or a
neat one, but it is fascinating, because this is the most dramatic episode
in the history of modern humans until then, in a period of roughly
300,000 years. It is possible that other regions where agriculture
developed early have equally fascinating backgrounds, but nowhere has
this modern human breakout moment been recorded, researched and

---

[2] If there were other centres of early farming in the region that were of an earlier period
or were equally prominent, they are yet to be discovered.

analysed as closely and graphically as in West Asia. We must follow that process of evolution to understand the nature of the agricultural transition, its world-altering consequences and, most importantly, its relationship with Mehrgarh. So here we go.

The archaeologists A. Nigel Goring-Morris and Anna Belfer-Cohen of the University of Jerusalem, who have written extensively on the emergence of the farming culture in the Levant, say: 'It is important to stress that developments appear to have been directional only in retrospect. The processes that took place were multifaceted, with various options available at the time; some of the choices, ultimately, were significant to future developments, but others were "sideshows" or culs-de-sac in the evolutionary sense. Accordingly, within the archaeological record, we may stumble on evidence for both categories.'[3] The authors then lay out the case for why the early processes of Neolithization – or farming transition – should be traced all the way back to around 20,000 years ago, during the last glacial period (29,000 to 14,000 years ago). 'This corresponds to a chronological span of some 15,000 years until the end of the Neolithic, that is, the equivalent of some 500–600 generations,' they say.

The story begins with hunter-gatherers in the Levant struggling with the stresses of the glacial period when many areas turned uninhabitable and resources became scarce. Population density in the habitable regions would have increased as existing populations crowded into these refuges as they retreated from elsewhere. Populations at this time would usually mean bands of twenty to thirty individuals, who may have had a larger social network of 250 to 500 individuals, which is necessary for a minimal sustainable mating network.

Increasing scarcity of habitable environments could have given the first impetus for a greater degree of sedentism – or being less mobile than earlier – and the rising population density could have triggered

---

[3] Nigel A. Goring-Morris and Anna Belfer-Cohen, 'Neolithization Processes in the Levant: The Outer Envelope', *Current Anthropology* (October 2011).

the search for better ways of gathering and processing food. As the climate started getting better slowly around 14,000 years ago, some of these experiments would have succeeded, while others failed. And those groups who had success with their experiments might have taken to a greater degree of sedentism, while others remained as mobile as earlier.

The Natufian culture that existed for about 3000 years from 12,500 BCE to 9500 BCE is often seen as the embodiment of this new dual style of living – with some sections of the population being sedentary and others remaining mobile to varying degrees. (Natufian comes from Wadi-an-Natuf, or the valley of Natuf, in Palestine, the area where the archaeologist Dorothy Garrod discovered cultural deposits of what she would in 1928 call the Natufian culture.) According to Goring-Morris and Belfer-Cohen, 'While some groups were more or less sedentary in favourable ecological settings (e.g., on the shores of lakes or marshes), others likely practised seasonal residential mobility, and still others on the margins were even more mobile.'

The Natufians had a large variety of groundstone utensils, especially mortars and pounding stones, suggesting that they were improving and intensifying their food processing techniques. They also had stone sickles – or stone blades inserted in bone handles – which suggests that they were harvesting something, perhaps reeds. It is unlikely that they were harvesting wild cereals because that would have led to sickle gloss (the sheen on a blade that is a by-product of cutting the stalks of cereals as they are rich in silica), which few, if any, of these implements had. There is also no evidence that they were doing any cultivation, though they had intensified the collection of plants just as they had intensified food processing.

There is reason to think that the sizes of at least some Natufian populations were increasing, and a sense of territoriality was becoming prevalent. For example, the Natufian sites began to have specially designated areas for burials. There were also exchange networks that were trading both utilitarian things such as stone utensils and exotic items such as molluscs, greenstone and other minerals. New cottage industries were emerging, with archaeological evidence suggesting an increased abundance of bone tool assemblages for basketry and matting. There is evidence for new fire technologies as well, such as lime-plaster production and the making of fired clay and ochre.

The Natufian culture, however, didn't survive long perhaps because of the deleterious effects of the dry, arid Younger Dryas phase (12,900 to 11,700 years ago). The early Natufian had large, well-built structures that were occupied by units bigger than nuclear families, but later on these units became smaller. There was also increasing mobility, while some areas were simply abandoned. The changing nature of Natufian culture was probably a result of the volatile nature of the climate and their response to it.

It wasn't just the Natufians in the Levant who were experimenting with new things. Excavations at the site of Abu Hureyra, near Mureybit on the Middle Euphrates, turned up evidence that around 11,000 BCE the residents here were harvesting wild wheat and rye. Rye, in fact, started showing signs of being domesticated as early as 10,700 BCE. There is still some debate about this among scientists and the issue is not settled, but if this finding is correct, it would be the earliest instance of domestication of any cereal. This didn't lead anywhere though – rye never became an important part of the agricultural package of west Asia, and Abu Hureyra itself was almost abandoned after the Younger Dryas.

The stresses of the Younger Dryas were soon put behind when the world started warming up again very rapidly around 11,700 years ago – raising the global temperature by as much as seven degrees Celsius on average. And very quickly, archaeologists say, we start seeing evidence of domesticated varieties of cereals or at least 'management' of wild varieties of plants and animals in the larger Fertile Crescent region. By 'management' they mean people taking care of wild plants and animals in a variety of ways with an intent to use them for later consumption. The different ways of management could range from deliberate cultivation to careful tending and harvesting of wild crops.

The earliest evidence for 'domesticated' wheat varieties – emmer and einkorn – come from sites in the Upper Euphrates valley in the Levant, dated to about 8500–8200 BCE. Securely dated domesticated barley is seen around 8000 BCE, by which time its presence is recorded throughout the Fertile Crescent and the Anatolian plateau.

The first evidence for domestication of goats, on the other hand, comes from the settlement of Ganj Dareh in the central Zagros mountain region and is dated to 7900 BCE. Archaeologists found in this natural habitat of goats the typical herding signature: early slaughter of young male goats and delayed slaughter of females. This is a strong signal of herding because herders usually cull the young males while keeping the females for breeding and perhaps milk consumption as well. A similar pattern was also observed in the settlement of Ali Kosh in south-western Iran, which was first occupied around 7500 BCE. Ali Kosh is outside the natural habitat of goats, which suggests that the pastoralists were already taking their herds to newer regions by then.

Both Ganj Dareh and Ali Kosh show evidence of full-fledged herding, but there are earlier signals of 'game management' that may not have gone as far as herding.[4] So one way or another, in the period between 8000 BCE and 7000 BCE, the evidence of goat domestication became widespread in the whole region, with goats replacing the hunted gazelle as the dominant presence in the animal remains of

---

[4] For example, at the Zawi Chemi Shanidar site in north-western Zagros, the archaeologist D. Perkins Jr found a prey profile focused only on two- to three-year-old male sheep, which is different from the usual pattern for hunting (mostly prime adult male) or herding (young males and older females). Another site at Hallan Cemi, 300 kilometres to the north-west of Zawi Chemi, also exhibited the same pattern. The archaeologist Richard Redding, who worked on the Hallan Cemi site, explains that this is a variation of the prime male hunting strategy, but one practised under conditions of extreme pressure on local herds. He argues that sedentary hunters intensively exploiting prime adult males in the region could have created a vacuum that attracted young males from other regions. Effectively, the hunting strategy could have created a 'male sink', assuring a continuous supply of young males, while keeping the herd itself robust and ongoing. This strategy of 'game management' has been observed in another site in the same region called Kortik Tepe as well (8900 BCE).

the settlements. The last regions to see this happen were the Levant (7200 BCE) and the eastern arm of the Fertile Crescent (7000 BCE).

According to the archaeologist Melinda A. Zeder, the evidence for cattle (*Bos taurus*) domestication in the region is still sketchy. In a 2011 paper, she wrote that although cattle remains from sites in the Upper and Middle Euphrates valley dated between 9000 BCE and 8000 BCE fall within the size range of wild aurochs (a Eurasian ox), at several sites there is evidence for a reduction in sexual dimorphism.[5] Cattle from other contemporary sites in the same region were still highly sexually dimorphic and could thus be seen as representing wild, hunted cattle. According to Zeder, domestic cattle slowly spread out of this heartland of initial domestication, getting to the southernmost reaches of the Levant only around 7500–7000 BCE at the earliest and the southern Zagros around 6500 BCE.

So the broad picture we see is that between 9500 BCE and 6500 BCE – that is, a 3000-year period immediately following the end of the Younger Dryas and the beginning of Holocene – both plant and animal domestication had spread across most of the Fertile Crescent, after progressing in fits and starts during the last glacial period, with different regions contributing in different ways at different times and probably with multiple instances of domestication for the same species.

As we saw, even as the transition was on, people were taking their plants and animals, perhaps still in the process of being domesticated and perhaps not even that, and migrating to newer places. Many places in the Fertile Crescent itself saw plants or animals being imported – an example being goats in the southern Levant. But the most interesting case of the introduction of plants and animals to a new area is Cyprus, where migrating humans brought with them both plants and animals, around 8500 BCE. Where the migrants came from is not clear, but there are indications that they could have been from north Levantine

---

[5] Melinda Zeder, 'The Origins of Agriculture in the Near East', *Current Anthropology* (October 2011).

littoral, which may have seen significant increases in population during that period.

Archaeological evidence on the ground shows that the incoming migrants brought with them domesticated barley and wheat (both einkorn and emmer) and wild but 'managed' cattle and goats. Zeder writes: 'This means that at the same time that the earliest morphologically domesticated einkorn and emmer is found in the Upper Euphrates valley (and even earlier than there is solid evidence for morphologically altered domestic barley) and when we see the first indications of animal management in the mainland Fertile Crescent, people were loading these managed plants and animals into boats and carrying them, along with the knowledge of how to successfully care for them, to an island 160 kilometres off the Levantine coast.'

None of these animals occurred naturally in Cyprus, so the confidence of the migrants in importing them and their success in exploiting them show that human control over these budding domesticates was more established than is apparent on the mainland, says Zeder.

Route to Mehrgarh

This is the background to be kept in mind while we go back to the question that started this discussion: where did the people of Mehrgarh come from? There are also a few other things to consider. For example, remember that the Kacchi plain where Mehrgarh is located is a semi-arid region even in today's wetter and warmer Holocene climate, so it is likely to have been desert-like until about 9700 BCE because of the glacial age and then the Younger Dryas. So whoever left behind the evidence of their settlement in Mehrgarh starting from around 7000 BCE couldn't have been thriving there for longer than a few thousand years before that. The region would have become significantly populated only when the climate changed, the deserts started turning green, the herbivores moved in looking for food and the carnivores followed them, looking for prey. And the humans, of course, followed all of them. So where could they have come from? There are two broad possibilities: they were either the First Indians, expanding their range westwards from their glacial age refuges in central, southern or eastern India, or they were the original inhabitants of Iran, expanding eastwards from their own refuges in the region. Or perhaps both happened simultaneously, or in quick succession, resulting in a mixed population.

One factor that is of importance while considering this issue is that Mehrgarh is on the edge of a west Asian climatic zone that is dominated by winter rains and winter crops. To its east is the Indian climatic zone, dominated by monsoons and summer rains and summer crops. For the First Indians, therefore, travelling north-west from central or southern India would have meant moving into unfamiliar territory. For the Iranians moving into the same region, though, it would have been just a range expansion, with no discernible change in climate or vegetation patterns. This is not to say, of course, that Mehrgarh couldn't have been populated by those moving in from the east, because if climatic zones had been an impenetrable factor for them, modern humans would never have got out of Africa in the first place.

So we need to look at other pieces of evidence to see how Mehrgarh could have come into being. But before we do that, let us remember that neither India nor Iran existed then and, therefore, these terms would be meaningless to the people moving into these regions. These terms are being used here merely as approximate geographical assignations to understand this period.

One obvious set of evidence to look for is similarities between what we find in Mehrgarh and what we find towards its east and its west. Towards the east the earliest evidence for agriculture is from Gujarat and eastern Rajasthan from around 3700 BCE; in southern and eastern India from around 3000 BCE; in Malwa, Madhya Pradesh, from around 2000 BCE; in the Vindhya region from around 1700 BCE; and in the Kashmir and Swat valleys from around 1500 BCE. (North-eastern India is too inadequately excavated to come to a conclusion on the beginnings of agriculture there.) All of these post-date Mehrgarh by thousands of years and, therefore, do not provide a platform for comparison.

The only region that could provide such a platform is the Middle Ganga region, where at Lahuradewa in the Sant Kabir Nagar district of Uttar Pradesh in the Upper Ganga plain there is indeed evidence for rice harvesting, sedentary settlement and ceramics dating back to about 7000 BCE. The chronology of the transition from harvesting wild rice to cultivating domesticated rice is not yet certain, but there is no doubt that Lahuradewa indicates experiments in agriculture were happening at several places in south Asia around the same time and that Mehrgarh was not alone. The only thing inhibiting its connection or comparison with Mehrgarh is the fact that the harvested plant/crop in Lahuradewa is rice, and not wheat or barley as in Mehrgarh, which later on became the mainstay of the Harappan Civilization.

Why didn't the Lahuradewa experiments lead to a rice-cultivation-based civilization of its own in the Middle Ganga region at this time? It is quite possible that for ecological or other reasons Lahuradewa could not develop a full agricultural package, with multiple crops and many domesticated animals as in Mehrgarh or west Asia. It could also be that the variety of rice that was grown at Lahuradewa was yet to reach its full productivity potential, which may have happened after hybridization with japonica rice which arrived from east Asia much later (see chapter 3, p. 157).

What about similarities with west Asia? Jarrige has this to say: 'In spite of some obvious differences, for instance the progressive predominance of the breeding of Zebu (*Bos indicus*), the full setting of the farming economy at Mehrgarh displays evident similarities with what had been noticed in the case of the early Neolithic settlements in the hilly regions forming the eastern border of Mesopotamia.'

For example, at the Ganj Dareh and Ali Kosh sites in the Deh Luran region of Iran at the foothills of the Zagros mountains, dated to around 7900 BCE, archaeologists have found the same kind of quadrangular houses built with narrow bricks about sixty centimetres long with finger marks for keying the mortar as was seen in Mehrgarh. Circular firepits filled with burnt pebbles that were found at Mehrgarh were also common at all these early settlements, and so were the traces of red paint found on the walls of the structures in Mehrgarh. Polished stone axes made in black diorite are found only in the upper levels of Period 1 in Mehrgarh and, similarly, in Ali Kosh, they are found only in the later phases, along with stone vessels. Only a few graves have been exposed at Ali Kosh, but they show skeletons placed in positions similar to those at Mehrgarh. Other similarities include ornaments made of seashells and semi-precious stones such as turquoise, a few beads in copper, baskets coated with bitumen and oblong-shaped cakes of red ochre.

The most striking parallels, however, could be the sequential slab construction method by which the earliest ceramics were made in Mehrgarh and at the foothills of the Zagros mountains and the building of big, multicellular granaries. Jarrige says the similarities between the sites on the eastern border of Mesopotamia – such as Ganj Dareh and Ali Kosh – and on the western margins of the Indus Valley – such as Mehrgarh – are 'significant'. He uses the phrase 'a sort of cultural continuum' to describe the relationship between the two regions in terms of the geographical context and the evolution of the sites over time.

It is, therefore, difficult to escape the conclusion that there were very close connections between the Mehrgarh Neolithic and west Asian Neolithic, but that should not take away from the fact that Mehrgarh had its own strong and striking characteristics, quite separate from those of west Asia. The domestication of the zebu cattle and possibly an indigenous goat variety, the early discovery and use of cotton, the dentistry and the profusion of craft activities and the quality of their work, all stand out and perhaps suggest 'an earlier, local background' as Jarrige puts it, that is yet to be fully understood. There is also little doubt that the water buffalo, as important a part of south Asia's food economy as the zebu cattle, was also domesticated in India, though whether this was done at Mehrgarh or somewhere in Gujarat is open to debate.

Similarities between two regions can occur either because of migrations or because of cultural diffusion, mediated perhaps by nomadic groups. So which one could it have been in Mehrgarh? That Mehrgarh was a little bit behind the developments in west Asia in chronological terms shows that, on current evidence, the flow of ideas in the early stages is more likely to have been from the west to the east, rather than from the east to the west. But that still does not answer the question whether the Neolithic transformation of Mehrgarh was accompanied by migrations of people. And there is only one way to settle this issue: DNA evidence, especially ancient DNA.

The story that DNA tells

There are three ways in which you can use DNA evidence to probe affinities between different populations and to trace migrations: analysis of uniparental DNA (Y-chromosome or mtDNA) of present-day populations, whole genome sequencing of present-day populations and DNA analysis of ancient human remains. Let us go through them one by one and see what they have to say about whether there was a migration of Iranian agriculturists into south Asia.

Uniparental DNA analysis looks at the haplogroups present in a population and analyses their family tree or phylogeny, and also maps their geographical distribution. As mentioned earlier, haplogroups identify a single line of descent either through the paternal line, from father to son to his son and so on (Y-chromosome), or through the maternal line, from mother to daughter to her daughter and so on (mtDNA).

Since mutations happen at a fairly predictable rate, these lines of descent branch out over time, forming clear family trees with the mutations being the nodes from where new branches sprout.

These branches and sub-branches are called macro-haplogroups, haplogroups or subhaplogroups or clades and they are named separately for Y-chromosome and mtDNA lineages. Geneticists have worked out Y-chromosome and mtDNA family trees that cover most of the modern human population based on current knowledge, and these are updated and expanded as new data comes in. Therefore, a geneticist can analyse the uniparental DNA of a person and decipher the macro-haplogroup, haplogroup and clade or subclade that he or she belongs to and, therefore, the family tree that he or she is part of. This is what happens, for example, when you hand over your DNA to a company that specializes in decoding your ancestry. (If two persons belong to the same mtDNA haplogroup, it means that they share a common female ancestor, and if two people belong to the same Y-chromosome haplogroup, it means that they share a common male ancestor, going back to the time when that haplogroup originated.)

And it's not just the family tree that can be worked out. Based on available data, we can also work out the 'phylogeography' of different haplogroups, which tells you not just to which branch of what family tree you belong, but also how that particular branch is distributed around the world today geographically and also how old a particular haplogroup or its subclade is. For example, we know that mtDNA haplogroup M2 is the most ancient haplogroup in the Indian subcontinent, that it arose around 60,200 years ago and that it is rarely found outside of South Asia.

The first method: Y-chromosome and mtDNA

The first method of getting an approximate idea of migrations is by accessing data on the distribution of various mtDNA and Y-chromosome haplogroups within a population and analysing their phylogeography. There are two pieces of data that could give clues about where a particular haplogroup or its subclade originated and how it spread: the relative frequency, or popularity, of the haplogroup in the different regions in which it is present and the variance within the haplogroup. Variance measures the diversity of subclades that a haplogroup has, and this is usually a function of the age of the haplogroup in a particular region and the population size. The higher the frequency and variance of a haplogroup in a particular region, the higher the likelihood that this region was a centre from which the haplogroup spread. Many such studies have been done in India, giving us some idea of the extent to which migrations may have shaped our demography.

For example, as mentioned earlier, we now know that 70 to 90 per cent of mtDNA haplogroups in Indian populations can trace their origin to the First Indians who arrived in India some 65,000 years ago. This means that only about 10 to 30 per cent of mtDNA lineages in the country are the result of later migrations. But the picture is radically different on the Y-chromosome side: as mentioned earlier, only 10 to 40 per cent of the Y-chromosome haplogroups in various Indian populations are descendant lineages of the First Indians. That means over 60 per cent of Y-chromosome haplogroups in the country are the result of later migrations. (There is a reason for this difference, which we will get into in chapter 4.)

We also know which haplogroups are likely to owe their origin to the First Indians and which ones are likely to be the result of later migrations. The 2017 paper by Marina Silva and others identified mtDNA haplogroups K2a5, U1a3a, H13a2a and R0a2 as Neolithic period migrations from west Asia, meaning they could be the mtDNA groups that came to India as part of farming-related migrations. The same study mentioned Y-chromosome haplogroups J2, L1a and L1c as the ones most likely to be associated with the spread of agriculture from west Asia.

But wait, as we discussed in chapter 1 (pp. 23–24), uniparental chromosomes mtDNA and Y-chromosome capture only a small part of the entire genome of individuals. So can we do whole genome analysis and see if those results too support the results of the uniparental DNA analysis? Yes, we can, as we shall find out now.

The second method: Whole genome data

There are two studies, one published in 2009 and the other in 2013, that did extensive sampling of present-day Indian population groups and used whole genome sequencing to reconstruct India's population history. Both papers had David Reich of the Harvard Medical School, K. Thangaraj and Lalji Singh of CCMB and Nick Patterson of the Broad Institute of Harvard and MIT as co-authors, among others.

The first paper was titled 'Reconstructing Indian Population History' and the second was titled 'Genetic Evidence for Recent Population Mixture in India'. Both studies emphasized one fact: everyone in India today is a mix, in different proportions, of ancestry related to at least two groups: the First Indians and west Eurasians.[6] The term west Eurasian includes west Asians such as people of the Fertile Crescent and Iran, as well as those from central Asia, the Caucasus and Europe. The studies showed that all population groups in India today have some amount of west Eurasian ancestry, varying from 20 per cent to 80 per cent, depending on the group. (Whole genome sequence data of present-day populations give us a general picture of affinities between different groups, though not a granular picture of how that affinity came about or who moved from where to where.)

But there were some twists in the story before this research conclusion was put to paper and it is worth following these twists to understand the political context of the discussions about migrations. The suggestion that modern Indians carry a significant amount of west-Eurasian-related ancestry was unpalatable to many, probably because it seemed to support the long-standing theory that it was a migration of Steppe pastoralists from central Asia sometime within the last 4000 years that brought Indo-European languages, including an early version of Sanskrit, and related cultural practices and concepts

---

[6] Present-day Indians also draw their ancestry from east Asia, but these two studies did not focus on that, so we will tackle this later.

to India. These Indo-European-language speakers called themselves Aryans, and for many in the right wing the idea that they came to India from elsewhere is unacceptable because they believe it would dethrone Sanskrit and the Vedas as the singular and fundamental source of Indian culture, as it would mean that the mighty Harappan Civilization that has left an indelible impression on Indian history and culture would have preceded their arrival.

Reich describes the reaction to the findings of the research in his 2018 book, *Who We Are and How We Got Here*:

The tensest twenty-four hours of my scientific career came in October 2008 when my collaborator Nick Patterson and I travelled to Hyderabad to discuss these initial results with Singh and Thangaraj.

Our meeting on October 28 was challenging. Singh and Thangaraj seemed to be threatening to nix the whole project. Prior to the meeting, we had shown them a summary of our findings, which were that Indians today descend from a mixture of two highly divergent ancestral populations, one being 'West Eurasians'. [The other being the First Indians.] Singh and Thangaraj objected to this formulation because, they argued, it implied that West Eurasian people migrated en masse into India. They correctly pointed out that our data provided no direct evidence for this conclusion. They even reasoned that there could have been a migration in the other direction, of Indians to the Near East[7] and Europe . . .

The cultural resonances of our findings gradually became clear to us. So we groped toward a formulation that would be scientifically accurate as well as sensitive to these concerns.

The next day, the full group reconvened in Singh's office. We sat together and came up with new names for ancient Indian groups. We wrote that the people of India today are the outcome of mixtures between two highly differentiated populations, Ancestral North

---

[7] Near East is equivalent to west Asia, the terminology used in this book.

Indians (ANI) and Ancestral South Indians (ASI), who before their mixture were as different from each other as Europeans and east Asians are today. The ANI are related to Europeans, central Asians, Near Easterners and people of the Caucasus, but we made no claim about the location of their homeland or any migration.

According to the study, the ASI were the descendants of the First Indians.

In essence, instead of stating that today's Indians are descendants of both the First Indians and west-Eurasian-related populations as the research suggested, the published paper created two new theoretically constructed population groups and said that today's Indians are the result of a mixture of two highly differentiated groups, ANI and ASI, with the ANI being closely related to west Eurasians. This was a scientifically defendable framework to understand the population structure of South Asia and to avoid a political controversy, but the cost of the compromise was that it made it easier to misinterpret the study. For instance, it left room for uninformed and false commentary in the news media that the ANI was a homogeneous and very ancient population group of India, like the ASI, which had settled here tens of thousands of years ago. This, despite the study itself stating clearly that the ANI could be a mixture of populations resulting from multiple migrations and may not be a homogeneous group, thus leaving open the possibility that some migrations could be as recent as within the last 4000 years.

Even with this formulation, the paper improved our understanding of Indian population formation, because it provided genetic evidence for a mixing of the descendants of the First Indians and other population groups who were closely related to the current-day populations of west Asia, Europe, the Caucasus and central Asia.

But this still left a problem, as those ideologically not ready to accept the idea of migrations into India could still assert that the direction of migration was from India to the rest of the world and this is what accounts for the close relationship between some population groups of India and those of west Asia, Europe, the Caucasus and central Asia. Whole genome data can prove affinity between population groups, but it cannot necessarily prove the direction of migration. As for uniparental data, large-scale population movements or natural calamities and epidemics that may have happened in the past could make it difficult to interpret the current-day distribution, frequency and variance data of haplogroups. So in addition to the two methods we have already discussed – uniparental DNA analysis based on present-day mtDNA and Y-chromosome lineages and whole genome sequencing of present-day populations – we need to look for a third method to settle the argument about the direction of migration, and there is, in fact, such a method: DNA analysis of ancient human remains. And to this we turn now.

The third method: Ancient DNA

Ancient DNA can settle questions about the direction of movement of peoples for the simple reason that with samples of DNA taken from ancient human skeletons at different time periods in a particular location, we can see how populations moved, on the ground, in the past. For example, if we see that ancient DNA from location X before 2000 BCE shows no evidence whatsoever for, say, any central Asian or Steppe lineage, and then from 1000 BCE onward we start seeing lots of evidence for that lineage, then we can clearly conclude that there was an influx of people with Steppe lineage into location X sometime between 2000 BCE and 1000 BCE.

The science of ancient-DNA took off only in the past five years or so. And since then, it has been rewriting history as we know it in continent after continent. The beauty of this process is that as more and more ancient DNA gets analysed across regions and continents, it is as if the pieces of a global historical puzzle are rapidly falling in place. The more the global migration picture gets filled, the more difficult it becomes to overturn the scientific consensus on how each region got populated.

The new ancient-DNA-based study that would settle long-standing questions about Indian prehistory was titled 'The Genomic Formation of South and Central Asia' and was posted on the preprint server for biology, bioRxiv, in March 2018. It was co-authored by ninety-two scientists from around the world and was co-authored and co-directed by David Reich, who runs a lab that currently has no equal in its ability to sequence and analyse DNA at scale and speed.

Notably, among the ninety-two co-authors were scientists from different disciplines who are stars in their own fields, such as James Mallory, archaeologist and author of the classic book *In Search of Indo-Europeans: Language, Archaeology and Myth*, and David Anthony, anthropologist and author of the ground-breaking book *The Horse, the Wheel and Language: How Bronze-Age[8] Riders from the Eurasian Steppes Shaped the Modern World*. Other well-known co-authors included the archaeobotanist Dorian Fuller and the archaeologist Nicole Boivin, who are familiar names in India owing to the work they have done in the country; Vasant Shinde, vice chancellor of the Deccan College, India's premier institution for archaeology; and Thangaraj of the CCMB, who was a co-director of the study as well. Niraj Rai of the Birbal Sahni Institute of Palaeosciences, Lucknow, Priya Moorjani of the University of California and Ayushi Nayak of the Max Planck Institute for the Science of Human History, Germany, were also co-authors. The study was lead-authored by Vagheesh Narasimhan of the Department of Genetics, Harvard Medical School.

The study was based on ancient DNA from 612 individuals. These ancient individuals came from many regions and periods: Iran and Turan, an old term for the region that includes Turkmenistan,

---

[8] The Bronze Age is a historical period characterized by the use of bronze. Different regions enter the Bronze Age at different times. In West Asia, South Asia and Europe, the Bronze Age begins approximately around 3200 BCE. The Bronze Age is often preceded by the Chalcolithic Age and is succeeded by the Iron Age.

Uzbekistan and Tajikistan (5600–1200 BCE); the Steppe east of the
Ural mountains, including Kazakhstan (4799–1000 BCE); and the
Swat valley of Pakistan (1200 BCE to 1 CE). This ancient DNA data
was then compared and co-analysed with genome-wide data from
present-day individuals – 1789 of them from 246 ethnographically
distinct groups in South Asia. It is this comparative analysis using
both ancient DNA and present-day DNA across regions and periods
that allowed the study to arrive at conclusions about who moved from
where and mixed with whom.[9]

So what did it find?

It found that an Iranian agriculturist population from around the
Zagros region had contributed significantly to the ancestry of the

---

[9] There has been criticism from some archaeologists and historians that the genetic
conclusions about ancient human migrations are based on too few ancient DNA
samples and are dependent on where ancient remains were chanced upon. According
to them, this is like looking for a watch you lost on a street, but only on those stretches
where there is lamplight. But to the extent that this argument is valid, it applies to
all of archaeology and prehistory in general – in these cases too, people are looking
for watches on streets, but only on those stretches where there is lamplight. More
seriously, there was a time, just a few years ago, when ancient DNA samples were
extremely sparse, but that is no longer the case. There is rapid discovery of ancient
DNA happening all across the world, and 'The Genomic Formation of South and
Central Asia' is based on ancient DNA from 612 individuals, which is a substantial
number. It is true that analysis of ancient DNA recovered directly from a Harappan
Civilization site is yet to be published, but we do have forty-one ancient DNA
samples from the Swat valley of Pakistan, dating from 1200 BCE. We also have three
samples of 'Indus Periphery' population that were recovered from Gonur and Shahr-
i-Sokhta. Studying all these in combination with extensive DNA analysis of present-
day populations is what allows scientists to arrive at reasonably robust conclusions.
They are robust partly because each new study based on ancient DNA is filling in
another part of the global puzzle of human migrations, and, therefore, conclusions
have to interlock if they are not to be disputed. In other words, the robustness of the
conclusions is more than it seems on the surface. However, as is the case in all of
science, in all disciplines at all times, all conclusions are conclusions based on current
evidence.

'Indus Periphery' population at least by between 4700 BCE and 3000 BCE. The study defines the 'Indus Periphery' population as migrants from the Harappan Civilization who were residents in neighbouring cities that the Harappans had trade and cultural relations with – such as Gonur and Shahr-i-Sokhta. Gonur is in Turkmenistan and was part of the Bactria–Margiana Archaeological Complex, a civilization that thrived between 2300 BCE and 1700 BCE. Shahr-i-Sokhta is a major archaeological site located in the south-eastern part of Iran which was occupied between 3200 BCE and 1800 BCE.

There were three ancient individuals from Gonur and Shahr-i-Sokhta that the researchers found to be Harappan migrants, and they were outliers when compared to the rest of the skeletons from the same sites because, unlike the others, they carried significant amounts of First Indian ancestry, apart from Iranian agriculturist ancestry. Since no ancient DNA has been recovered from the Harappan Civilization areas so far, these 'Indus Periphery' individuals stand in as proxy for the Harappan population itself.[10] So that answers the question we started with: was there a migration of Iranian agriculturists into India? Yes, because ancient DNA shows that the Harappans harboured significant Iranian agriculturist ancestry. Now let us look more closely at how exactly ancient DNA helped the researchers arrive at this conclusion. The ancient DNA of people from the Zagros region of Iran between 7000 BCE and 8000 BCE showed that they harboured a distinctive type of west Eurasian ancestry. They were different from the others in the Fertile Crescent region because they lacked the Anatolian ancestry that everyone else had. In fact, Anatolian ancestry can be seen spread all the way from Anatolia (today's Turkey) to eastern Iran and far-eastern Turan. But the ancestry keeps declining as you move from the west to the east – it ranges from 70 per cent in Anatolia to 33 per cent in

---

[10] Scientists have managed to recover DNA from the Harappan site of Rakhigarhi in India, but the study has not yet been published. Credible news reports about the unpublished study, however, suggest they support the conclusion of a mixing between Zagros agriculturists and the Harappans.

Iran and 3 per cent in far-eastern Turan. The reason for this pattern of distribution of Anatolian ancestry could be that Anatolians had played a role in spreading agriculture towards the east (just as they had also spread it towards the west, into Europe). But remember, the Zagros population between 7000 BCE and 8000 BCE was unaffected by this genetic spread.

We can now look at the other crucial bits of evidence – the ancient DNA from Gonur and Shahr-i-Sokhta. In all, the study had access to the DNA of sixty-nine ancient individuals from BMAC sites and a great majority of them had this particular combination of ancestries: early-Iranian-agriculturist-related ancestry (about 60 per cent), Anatolian agriculturist-related ancestry (about 21 per cent) and west-Siberian-related ancestry (about 13 per cent).

The remains of the three individuals from Gonur and Shahr-i-Sokhta were dated to between 3100 BCE and 2200 BCE. These individuals, in contrast to the rest, had between 14 and 42 per cent of their ancestry related to the First Indians and 58 to 86 per cent of their ancestry related to Iranian agriculturists. Since they had no Anatolian ancestry, it was clear to the researchers that they came from farther east since Anatolian ancestry keeps declining towards the east. That they had significant First Indian ancestry also suggested the same – that they came from the east, from the Harappan Civilization, and were migrants to Gonur and Shahr-i-Sokhta. In other words, the study showed that the Harappan population from around 3100–2200 BCE had part ancestry from the Zagros agriculturists, while there was no indication of a First Indian ancestry in the Zagros agriculturist ancient DNA dating to 7000–8000 BCE. The direction of migration, therefore, was clear. People had migrated from the Zagros region of Iran towards India.

There was more evidence. The study had access to the DNA of forty-one ancient individuals from the Swat valley, who lived approximately between 1200 BCE and 800 BCE – about a millennium later than the outliers in BMAC and more than half a millennium after the Harappan Civilization started declining around 1900 BCE. These were genetically very similar to the three outlier samples from Gonur and Shahr-i-Sokhta, with major components of their ancestry being related to Iranian agriculturists and First Indians. (They also had a 22 per cent ancestry from the Steppe-Middle-to-Late-Bronze-Age people – the result of a later admixture that could have happened in the second millennium BCE, which we will talk about in chapter 4.)

In sum, forty-four individuals from the 'Indus Periphery' (BMAC, Shahr-i-Sokhta) and Swat valley during the period ranging from 3100 BCE to 800 BCE carried evidence of a significant mixing between Iranian agriculturists and the First Indians. And genetic modelling showed that the 'Indus Periphery' population would fit well as one of the ancestral groups of the present-day Indian population.

Here's a recap then of how these new findings add greater detail to what we already knew. As we saw earlier, genetic studies based on present-day haplogroups had suggested significant migrations that brought new lineages to India. And studies based on whole genome sequencing of present-day populations had shown that Indians today are a mixture of First Indians and populations that are closely related to present-day west Eurasians. But these studies could not conclusively answer questions involving the direction of migration. What the latest ancient DNA-based study has done is exactly that: given a definitive answer to the question of the direction of migration, while also providing a finer understanding of the multiple migrations that caused the affinity between present-day Indians and west Eurasians. We now know that there was a migration of Iranian agriculturists from the Zagros region to the Indus Valley. From the Swat samples, we also know there was a migration from the Steppe, which we will talk about in detail later.[11]

---

[11] To use a more technical description, we now know that the ancestry of ASI derives from First Indians (Ancient Ancestral South Indians or AASI) and Iranian agriculturists. And we also know that the ancestry of ANI comes from First Indians (AASI), Iranian agriculturists and Steppe pastoralists. Almost all present-day

When could the mixing between Iranian agriculturists and First Indians have taken place? By looking at the genetic data of the three outlier individuals from the BMAC and Shahr-i-Sokhta, geneticists can determine the latest period by which the mixing could have happened. And that works out to between 4700 BCE and 3000 BCE. (Genetics hasn't been able to work out a similar period for the earliest period by which mixing could have happened.) But as we have seen, there is evidence for the beginnings of agriculture at Mehrgarh much earlier, from around 7000 BCE. So agriculture in Mehrgarh or elsewhere in the region could either have been begun locally by the First Indians with migrating agriculturists from the Zagros region arriving only later, or Iranian agriculturists may have moved into the region and brought with them some agricultural practices before mixing later with the First Indians, some of whom, we know, were experimenting with agriculture in places such as Lahuradewa. Of course, it could also mean that the Iranian agriculturists from Zagros arrived around 7000 BCE and mixed with First Indians around that time itself, since genetics hasn't provided the earliest date of the mixing. There is no reason to assume that agriculture only began in one place and then spread everywhere else. It is more likely that agriculture had multiple origins, around the same time, with different degrees of success in terms of productivity and, hence, population expansion.

In all of these possible scenarios, it is clear that at some point in the trajectory of agriculture in the north-western region of South Asia, whether right at the beginning or later, there was a significant influx of Iranian agriculturists from the Zagros region whose genetic imprint on the Indian population today is writ large.

But hold on, before we conclude this chapter, just one more bit of evidence to complete the loop. Remember we had said that earlier uniparental chromosome studies had thrown up J2, L1 and L1c as the

---

populations of Indians are a mixture of ANI and ASI, in different proportions in different regions and communities.

Y-chromosome lineages that are likely to have come from west Asia to India? So what does the ancient DNA evidence have to say about this? What haplogroups did the ancient outlier individuals from Gonur and Shahr-i-Sokhta belong to? Only two of them were male, and we know what their Y-chromosome haplogroup is. It is J2, just as the uniparental DNA study had suggested! Looking back, one can say that after the initial arrival of modern humans in the subcontinent around 65,000 years ago, and after the invention of microliths that probably led to their unquestioned supremacy in the region and their growth in population, the start-up at Mehrgarh was the most consequential development, a definitive turning point, in the prehistory of India.

The residents of Mehrgarh who raised the first mud-brick homes of two or three rooms may not have realized it then, but they were laying the foundation for the first efflorescence of civilization in South Asia, called the Harappan Civilization, or the Indus Valley Civilization. It took about 4500 years, or over 150 generations, for those humble mud-brick abodes to turn into the urban structures of a Harappa or a Mohenjo-daro or a Dholavira and there must have been many twists and turns along the way. But once agriculture took root, and modern humans started creating a surplus that they could save and invest, the wheels of history started spinning fast – which would, of course, lead to the invention of the wheel itself!

But what kind of a civilization did it lead to, and how? To that we turn in the next chapter.

Postscript: When the Harappan Civilization fell apart after 1900 BCE, the people who built it and kept it going for centuries spread out to the rest of the subcontinent – to the east and the south, in particular. To use the imagery with which we began this chapter, the people of the Harappan Civilization – a mix of the descendants of the First Indians and the Iranian agriculturist migrants – therefore became the sauce that was spread all over the crust of the pizza that is the Indian population. We will discuss this further in the epilogue.

3

The First Urbanites: The Harappans

How the largest civilization of its time, with a unique set of practices and outlook, took wing. And how its creators spread the Dravidian languages and became the ancestors of both North Indians and South Indians.

It took nearly 5000 years for the seeds that were planted – literally – in the Kacchi plain of Balochistan around 7000 BCE to grow into the mighty tree that was the Harappan Civilization between 2600 and 1900 BCE.

Not all agricultural societies become civilizations, but no civilization can become one without passing through the stage of agriculture. (We'll come to precisely what a civilization is on p. 117. For the moment let's take the term at face value.) This is because at some stage in the development of agriculture, as productivity improves, not all people would need to be engaged in producing or procuring food. A significant number of people could be freed up to pursue other activities such as building walls or monuments for new cities; making new tools, weapons and jewellery; organizing long-distance trade; creating new artistic masterpieces; coming up with new inventions; keeping accounts; and perhaps constructing new public infrastructure such as

Ruins of the city of Mohenjo-daro. The Harappan Civilization was the
largest civilization of its time.

irrigation canals that further improve the productivity of agriculture,
thus releasing even more people to do new things.

This can happen, of course, only if a society that has transitioned to
high-productivity agriculture has also, at some stage in its evolution,
found a way to channel the bonanza of free time into other work
fruitfully. In the ancient world, this often involved creating new
ideologies and new hierarchies or power structures to coerce or
otherwise convince large groups of people to devote their time to the
new tasks for very little reward. Religion often came in handy in this
process and so, sometimes, did violence.

Since the script used by the Harappans has not yet been deciphered
despite nearly a century of concentrated effort by experts from around
the world, we do not have enough direct, written evidence about the
new ideology and power relationships that accompanied the emergence

of the urban civilization of Harappa. But we get glimpses of their ideology and clues about the power structure from the seal motifs, designs, architecture and sculptures they left behind.

Almost every step of the physical, material processes that led from the two-room brick houses and barley fields of Mehrgarh to the monumental structures of cities like Harappa, Mohenjo-daro and Dholavira has been well documented archaeologically, with no major breaks or gaps in between. We can see, on the ground, farming villages spreading from the Kacchi plain to other parts of Balochistan, the Indus Valley, the Ghaggar–Hakra valley, Gujarat and beyond. Over thousands of years, they slowly grew into different regional cultures with walled towns and different styles of pottery. Then around 2600 BCE, these individual cities coalesced into what would come to be called the Harappan Civilization, spread across a vast region lying mostly along the valleys of two major river systems – the Indus, which still continues to flow, and the Ghaggar–Hakra, which has mostly gone dry since. At its peak, the civilization covered much of Pakistan, north-eastern Afghanistan and western India, including mainly the states of Punjab, Rajasthan, Haryana, Uttar Pradesh and Gujarat.

This continuity shows that the people who built one of the earliest, largest and most remarkable civilizations of the ancient world did not suddenly appear from elsewhere; they were here for long and they built it from scratch. The earlier assumption that the Harappan Civilization was an offshoot of the Mesopotamian Civilization has, therefore, been proved wrong (the Mesopotamian Civilization lasted from around 4000 BCE to arguably 330 BCE when the region was conquered by Alexander, and it spanned Iraq, Kuwait, northern Saudi Arabia, south-eastern Turkey, eastern Syria and parts of Iran). There are no mysteries about the development of the Harappan Civilization that would be solved by the assumed migration of later-day city builders from Mesopotamia.

Of course, as we saw in chapter 2, the people of the Harappan Civilization were themselves a mixture of agriculturists from the

Zagros mountains of Iran and the descendants of the First Indians. But that admixture happened millennia before the first cities of the Harappan Civilization went up and, therefore, it would make no sense to describe the population as anything but South Asian – just as it would make no sense to treat Asian, European and American civilizations as African since all modern humans originally came from there.

This is not to say that there were no contacts between the Mesopotamian Civilization and the Harappan Civilization. The significant trade relations between the two have left behind many archaeological footprints and there are symbolic or cultural artefacts which clearly show influences that run both ways. For example, there are Mesopotamian seals that show the water buffalo, a natural resident of the Indus Valley and not Mesopotamia. In one Mesopotamian seal, a hero grapples with a buffalo, while in another, nude heroes slake the thirst of water buffaloes. Both seals belong to the period of the Akkadian emperor Sargon.

Imprint of an Akkadian period Mesopotamian cylinder seal
(ca. 2350–2000 BCE). The seal depicts two kneeling nude heroes holding
vessels from which spurts water to quench the thirst of two buffaloes.

The Metropolitan Museum of Art, New York

Left: An Akkadian period Mesopotamian cylinder seal, ca. 2250–2150 BCE.
Right: Impression of the cylinder seal. On the left of the impression is a bull-man in combat with a lion. On the right is a bearded nude hero subduing a water buffalo that is standing on its hind legs.

Asko Parpola, author and emeritus professor of South Asian studies at the University of Helsinki, explains it this way: 'It has been plausibly suggested that Harappans brought some water buffaloes from the Indus Valley by ship, given that Sargon boasts that ships came from far-off Meluhha to his new capital, Akkad.' Meluhha was the name by which the Harappan Civilization was known to the west Asians and there are many references to it in Mesopotamian records – including an inscription on a cylinder seal that reads 'Su-ilisu, interpreter of the Meluhhan language'.

There is also evidence of elephants, rhinoceroses and peacocks reaching Mesopotamia from Meluhha. And it was not just animals and birds. Mario Liverani, professor of ancient Near East history at the Sapienza University of Rome, says sesame, a plant of South Asian origin, came to Mesopotamia via the Indus Valley, and was acclimatized to the new environment as a summer crop. 'Seasonally it fitted well with cereal cultivation, which took place in the winter,' writes Liverani in *Uruk: The First City*.

On the other hand, there are five seals from Mohenjo-daro and six moulded tablets from Harappa depicting a hero holding off two tigers on his right and left with bare hands, and these are strikingly similar to the seals of Mesopotamia and the mythology around the Sumerian king Gilgamesh.[1] In the Mesopotamian seals, the king is usually holding off lions instead of tigers in the same manner, but there are no depictions of lions in the Harappan Civilization. It is, of course, possible – as the archaeologist and author Jonathan Mark Kenoyer argues – that the tale of a hero dealing with ferocious animals in this manner is a myth that predates both civilizations and goes back to the hunter-gatherer period, and that both the Mesopotamians and the Harappans were interpreting this in their own manner in their artefacts.

The way in which some men in both Harappan and Mesopotamian sculptures wear their upper cloth is also strikingly similar, with the robe being drawn over their left shoulder and under the right arm, leaving the right shoulder bare. The distinctive trefoil design (a three-leaf clover) on the robe worn by the *Priest King*, one of the most magnificent sculptures recovered from Mohenjo-daro, is found in Mesopotamia as well. Says Asko Parpola in *The Roots of Hinduism*, 'West Asian gods and divine kings had festive clothes with golden stars, rosettes and so forth sewn on to them, which were known in Sumerian and Akkadian as "sky garments" . . . The cloak of the "priest-king" statue from Mohenjodaro is clearly a form of "sky-garment" decorated with trefoils, originally filled with red paste.'

---

[1] Sumerians were the people who lived in the heartland of Mesopotamia, between the rivers Euphrates and Tigris, the region that is today called Iraq. They built the first cities of the Mesopotamian Civilization, such as Uruk. They were succeeded by the Semitic-language-speaking Akkadians, with their capital at Akkad. The Akkadian empire was founded by Sargon, who brought the cities of Sumer also under his control. Akkadian gradually replaced Sumerian as a spoken language and the Sumerians were no longer heard of.

A dagger with an ivory handle and flint blade from Egypt, ca. 2750 BCE, perhaps showing contemporary Mesopotamian influence. The bearded figure of a priest-king wears Mesopotamian clothing and is flanked on both sides by lions he is subduing.

A Harappan Civilization seal depicting a man subduing tigers on his right and left

The hairstyle of some men on the Harappan sculptures – the plaited double bun or chignon – is also found in Mesopotamian sculptures, including one of Emperor Sargon himself in the city of Susa. The Dutch archaeologist Elisabeth C.L. During Caspers describes the hairstyle thus: 'The hair is dressed in a bun, which is then secured horizontally, by means of a ribbon or hair-slide of some sort, resulting in the division of hair into two protuberances one above the other.'[2]

But these possible proofs of cultural interaction and influence both ways do not change the fact that the Harappan Civilization in its essence was unique and significantly different from the civilization to its west.

The Louvre, Paris / Wikimedia Commons

A fragment of the 'Stele of Vultures' from Mesopotamia, ca. 2450 BCE. This stele to commemorate the victory of a Sumerian city state against its neighbour depicts two men (top right and bottom right) wearing their hair in a double-bun style.

---

[2] Elisabeth C.L. During Caspers, 'Sumer, Coastal Arabia and the Indus Valley in Protoliterate and Early Dynastic Eras: Supporting Evidence for a Cultural Linkage', *Journal of the Economic and Social History of the Orient*, 22(2), 1979.

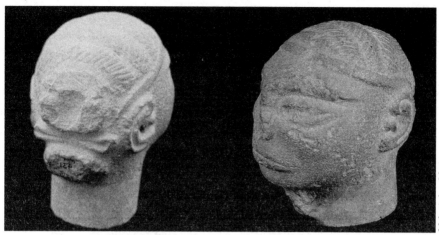

Mohenjodaro Museum

A sculpture from Mohenjo-daro depicting a man wearing his hair in a double-bun style.

A civilization like no other

Let us count the ways in which it is so. Unlike the Mesopotamians with their monumental ziggurats (houses for the patron gods and goddesses of each city), the Harappans have nothing that can be identified as grand temples or even large ritual places. Thirty-two ziggurats have been discovered so far in Mesopotamia – twenty-eight in Iraq and four in Iran – but not even a single structure has been clearly identified as a temple in the vast expanse of the Harappan Civilization.

Neither were there clearly recognizable palaces for the kings in the Harappan Civilization, again quite unlike in Mesopotamia. The Harappans also did not set up sculptures glorifying kings and their exploits, unlike in the civilization to its west. Even the well-known and skilfully carved *Priest King* sculpture of Mohenjo-daro is no more than seventeen and a half centimetres in height and eleven centimetres in width! And there is no way to even tell whether it represents a king or a priest or a nobleman. Most archaeologists would only go as far as to say that the sculpture might represent a prominent member of the ruling elite of Mohenjo-daro.

Bust of the priest-king from Mohenjo-daro. He is depicted wearing
a trefoil-patterned robe and a ribbon headband with a central ornament
as well as an ornament on his upper arm.

What about elaborate funerals for the royals, a major feature of west
Asia and Egypt? No, there are no signs of ostentatious and elaborate
funerals for anyone in the Harappan Civilization, and no pyramids
for departed leaders either as in Egypt. In Mesopotamia, the royals
were buried with enormous hoards of precious jewellery, artefacts and
sometimes even their servants – all to meet their corporeal needs in
the afterlife. In the Harappan Civilization, by contrast, burials are
often accompanied by pottery containing food for the afterlife and
not much more, though people were often interred with their personal

ornaments. There is nothing remotely suggestive of the kind of royal funerals that seem to have been common in west Asia. The historian Shereen Ratnagar says in *Understanding Harappa* that graves had an average of fifteen pots, with some provision of food and drink for the departed, including joints of meat. The pottery found in the graves included lavishly painted dishes on stands, squat, bulging jars and S-profile jars. Ornaments were never in profusion, and tools were few.

If you think this is because Harappans didn't know how to make precious jewellery and artefacts you would be wrong! Quite a few pieces of jewellery and ornaments found in the royal burials of west Asia came from the Harappan Civilization. In fact, jewellery made of carnelian, turquoise, lapis lazuli and other precious stones and shells was a major item of export for the Harappans and its cities had lots of workshops for making it. It is just that the Harappans, like the Chinese, preferred to hand down their precious possessions to their descendants rather than bury them. When people got tired of their heirlooms, they probably recycled them to make new items too.

This is, of course, bad news for archaeologists and historians. The royal burials of west Asia and the pyramids of Egypt have been enormously helpful in bringing alive that period of world history. By contrast, precious items and even bronze and other metal items are under-represented in the Harappan Civilization because archaeologists can find them only in those rare circumstances where ancient individuals buried their treasures, often in their own houses, and then failed to recover them for whatever reason. Sometimes, archaeologists also stumble upon items that have ended up in the trash heap or have been lost in the streets. As you can imagine, such artefacts cannot match the richness and variety of royal burials intended to provide the dead with enough resources for their afterlife.

A striking feature of the Harappan Civilization that sets it apart from its contemporaries is the lack of representation of violence between humans. There are many Harappan seals that depict violence, but these involve supernatural beings in conflict with each other or humans attacking animals or humans and supernatural beings in combat, not humans in conflict with other humans.

There is one seal that is an exception to this rule, though, and in it two men, with hair worn in the double-bun style, are spearing each other, while they are both being held by the hand by a female figure, perhaps a deity, wearing a headdress with a long pendant. It could also be that they are holding the female figure by the hand, rather than the other way around. This has been interpreted variously as a conflict over a woman or even as a scene of human sacrifice.

This near absence of representation of human-on-human violence is also reflected in the lack of evidence of war weaponry such as battleaxes or swords. The weapons that the Harappans had were spears, knives and arrows, all necessary for hunting animals or even winning a fight with a rival, but perhaps not sufficient for war, says Kenoyer, who also points out that in the 700 years of the Harappan

Archaeological Survey of India

Imprint of a cylinder seal from Kalibangan depicting a woman standing between two men who are about to spear each other.

Civilization's existence – between 2600 BCE and 1900 BCE – there is no evidence that any of its cities were attacked or burnt down.

Public infrastructure, not private palaces

Now that we know what the Harappans did not have, let us look at what they had that was unique to them. What did they excel in? Here's a partial list.

To begin with, they had well-planned cities with neatly laid out streets and residences that were often, though not always, in a north–south and east–west grid-like pattern. They had highly evolved water management technology that hasn't been seen anywhere else in the ancient world, with Dholavira in Gujarat being an outstanding example. With scanty monsoon rains, and two seasonal streams on either side, Dholavira did everything it could to make its water last, including damming the streams. Inside the fortified walls of the city,

The Great Bath of Mohenjo-daro

it had many interconnected reservoirs, with the eastern reservoir (seventy-four metres long, twenty-six metres wide and seven metres deep) being the largest of its kind in the ancient world. It also had underground storage systems. The storm water drain at Dholavira was made of dressed stone and was more than five feet in height, and you can walk inside it. All these used the natural incline of the site to regulate the flow of water from one place to another.

The 700-odd wells and the Great Bath of Mohenjo-daro in Sindh also stand testimony to the unique attention the Harappans paid to water. Residents of Harappa, who lived in houses (some of them two storeys high or more) with rooms arranged around a central courtyard, had separate channels for water supply and for sewage disposal. On this topic it is worth quoting the historian Upinder Singh from her book *A History of Ancient and Early Medieval India*:

A reservoir with steps leading into it, Dholavira

Many houses or groups of houses had separate bathing areas and toilets. Bathing platforms with drains were often located in rooms next to a well. The floor of the bathing area was usually made of tightly fitted bricks, frequently set on edge, to make a carefully sloped watertight surface. A small drain led from here, cut through the house wall, and went out into the street, connecting ultimately with a larger sewage drain . . .

Recent excavations in Harappa have uncovered toilets in almost every house. The commodes were made of big pots sunk into the floor, many of them associated with a small, lota-type jar, no doubt for washing up. Most of the pots had a small hole in the base through which water could seep into the ground . . .

Singh mentions that archaeologists found 'lotas' at the bottom of the internal latrines that the homes were provided with, suggesting that

The drainage system of Mohenjo-daro

Larry Burrows / The LIFE Picture Collection / Getty Images

the way South Asians wash themselves hasn't changed all that much
– even if many South Asians today do not have the indoor facilities
that the Harappans enjoyed. And not just the residents. Kenoyer says
there were bathing platforms and public wells for the convenience of
visitors and traders too in Harappa. No contemporary civilization,
whether Egyptian, Mesopotamian or Chinese, had anything similar
on offer when it came to public conveniences for residents or guests.

Even more striking than the civic amenities, perhaps, is another feat
of the Harappans: uniform weights. Across the length and breadth of
this largest of civilizations there was only one way to weigh materials,
using standardized cubic weights made of chert (a type of rock).
The cities of Mesopotamia, by contrast, had a medley of weighing
systems, differing both by region and by the commodity that was to
be weighed. By avoiding unnecessary conversions between different
weighing standards when traders moved from one city to another, the

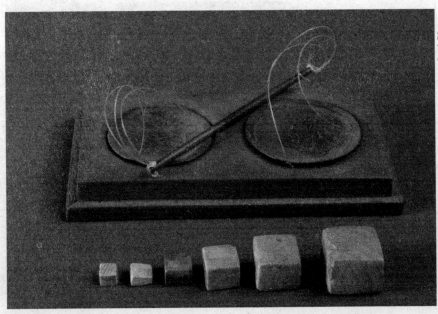

Balance scale and weights from the Harappan Civilization

Harappans must have significantly reduced the transaction costs of business. If there were an 'ease of doing business' ranking in the third millennium BCE, the Harappans would have been front runners, along with the Egyptians perhaps, who also had a similar, standardized weighing system.

As ubiquitous as the weights in Harappan cities were the bangles – hundreds of thousands of them. If you think bangles are nothing unique, you would be wrong. As Kenoyer says, 'If I call my friends in Egypt and ask them how many bangles did you excavate, they may say, a dozen or one or two. In China, you may find one or two. In Mesopotamia, you may find a few. But in the Indus Valley, we find hundreds of thousands of bangles. They were distinctive ornaments and they were for both females and males.'

We can go on listing an endless variety of things that are unique to the Harappans and are still clearly recognizable as 'Indian' by us in the twenty-first century – from seals that show veneration for the peepul tree to the 'handi' or the cooking pot 'with a ridge on the top that deflects the fire so that the ridge doesn't get hot and you can pick

National Museum of Pakistan, Karachi / Robert Harding / Alamy Stock Photo

A bangle from the Harappan Civilization

it up', as Kenoyer explains. The pottery styles differed across Harappan cities, but the 'handi' design was so popular that these cooking pots could be found everywhere.

Perhaps the most important distinction of the Harappan Civilization was its sheer size – at its height, it may have covered almost a million square kilometres, more than the Mesopotamian and Egyptian civilizations combined. The Harappan Civilization is also likely to have had the largest population of any contemporary civilization – which is not surprising, considering that we were the largest modern human population even as far back as 20,000 years ago, as we saw in chapter 1. South Asia being the centre of modern human population is not a new phenomenon – it is just an ancient track record that we continue to maintain.

To get a sense of how big an area the civilization occupied, remember that today's India covers about three million square kilometres. The Harappan Civilization covered about a third of that. Imagine what it would have taken to knit together such a large civilization through common standards of weights, seals, script, city design and even burnt bricks which had a uniform height to width to length ratio of 1:2:4. And all this without modern methods of communication and travel. Despite the geographical range of the civilization, it seems to have been less conflict-prone than its western counterparts.

Was it also less unequal than its western counterparts? The answer to that is not clear. The lack of palaces and ostentatious burials could suggest a less unequal society, but the unequal sizes of residences in the cities and the importance of status goods such as precious jewellery suggest otherwise. Most historians today believe that the Harappan Civilization was held together by an 'elite group' rather than one powerful king controlling the different 'city states'.

So whichever way you look, the Harappan Civilization seems to have sprung from very different impulses and instincts than other contemporary civilizations and the Harappans seem to have made different choices about the kind of society they wanted to live in. But how did a collection of farming villages evolve into something that can be called a civilization? And what exactly do we mean by 'civilization' anyway? Why do we often proclaim that the Indian civilization is about 5000 years old and not, say, 9000 years old when agriculture began, or, say, about 2300 years old when the Mauryas built the first Indian empire?

The word 'civilization' is etymologically connected to 'city', so one could say civilization presupposes an urban transition – or an 'urban revolution' as Gordon Childe, the prehistorian admiringly called the 'great synthesizer', described it in the 1930s. According to Childe, the earliest cities of the world exhibited the following characteristics: a population that is often hundreds of times larger than any village; full-time specialists such as craftsmen, merchants, officials and transport workers; a ruling class that accumulates the surplus production of the peasants; monumental public buildings; systems of recording and writing without which it would be impossible to manage a city; full-time artists – sculptors, painters, seal engravers – who created things in a style that is unique and specific to a particular civilization; and foreign trade to get materials not available locally. Each of these attributes applies to all the major Harappan sites – from Harappa and Mohenjo-daro to Dholavira, Rakhigarhi and Kalibangan.

The first 'city' in the world by this definition would be Uruk in Lower Mesopotamia – perhaps better known as the capital city of Gilgamesh, the mythic hero of *The Epic of Gilgamesh*. At the height of its power, around 3200 BCE, Uruk would have had tens of thousands of people within its walls, much like Harappa or Mohenjo-daro around 2600 BCE.

So when we say the Indian civilization is 5000 years old, what we mean is that the first cities of the Harappan Civilization were going up around then. This is broadly correct, though what is usually called the Mature Harappan phase of the civilization began only around 2600 BCE, that is, about 4600 years ago. It is around this time that the usage of a common script and common seals became prevalent across the cities of the civilization, but many elements that go into the making of a civilization were already in process by then.

For example, we see the first markings on post-fired pottery that would later develop into a script as early as 3300 BCE in Harappa, around the same time when early writing begins in Mesopotamia, Egypt and China. We also see the first massive walls being built around two separate areas adjacent to each other in Harappa around 2800 BCE. It would have taken 450 men around three months to build these walls and these could not have been constructed without the ability to make and transport bricks on a very large scale. There is indeed evidence to suggest that by this time ox carts and bullock carts were in extensive use. There are terracotta toy-cart fragments from Harappa and cartwheels from Girawad in Haryana dated to around 3700 BCE. This is around the same time that wheeled carts start making an appearance in Mesopotamia and elsewhere.

If you want to get a sense of the grandeur that was the Harappan Civilization, the one place in India where you need to go is Dholavira in the Great Rann of Kutch in Gujarat, a seven-hour drive from Ahmedabad or a distance of about 350 kilometres. It is situated on the island of Khadir, surrounded by salt plains, and you have to drive through the stunning landscape of the White Rann to reach there. The long, straight, almost empty road cuts through the flat land, with the sunlight reflecting off the unending terrain of white salt on both sides. You begin to wonder 'Why did anyone bother to build a city in such a remote place?' before you remember the answer: what are today salt marshes were about four metres under water when the city was thriving, thus making the city a crucial hub for the Harappan Civilization's substantial overseas trade with Mesopotamia.

Once you reach Dholavira, you feel you have fallen down a wormhole and have emerged on the other side of space-time. It is the grandest Harappan site on Indian soil and your heart beats faster as you walk around the ruins and see what your ancestors were up to some 4500 years ago (yes, it is right to call them our ancestors, and we will come to that later in this chapter). More than anything else, it is the scale of the ruins and the perfection and robustness of the walls and foundations that are still standing that strikes one. The ruins are spread over nearly 100 hectares, with the fortified city – divided into a 'citadel' on a raised platform, a 'middle town' and a 'lower town' – occupying about half of it.

The 'citadel', with its own additional fortification, is further divided into a 'castle', which may have been where the ruling elite lived, and a 'bailey', which seems to have been the quarters for important officials. Of course, these names were given by archaeologists and we do not know what the residents called them, and we are not even fully sure that the buildings were put to the kind of use that we think they were. For example, there is a large stadium that separates the citadel from the middle town and which has stands for seating spectators. It is reasonable to think that this might have been used for public ceremonies or spectacles of some kind. Of course, it could have been used as a market on some days too. There are also several large reservoirs, three of which have been excavated. Dholavira, like other Harappan sites in Gujarat but unlike sites elsewhere, made extensive use of sandstone in its architecture, along with mud brick. Most Harappan cities, by contrast, are built with sun-baked or fire-burnt bricks.

It is clear that the city was built to a plan (like many other Harappan sites) and did not haphazardly evolve over time. The archaeologist R.S. Bisht, who headed the Dholavira excavation, describes the city thus: 'Excellent town planning with mathematical precision. The entire site was mapped out and divided into squares and triangles and there was a definite ratio and proportion to each minor or major division.' The people who conceived of the city and built it seem to have thought and acted on such a scale that after Dholavira went into decline around 1900 BCE, like the rest of the Harappan cities, we had to wait for another millennium and a half or so, until the Mauryas came along, to see architecture of such scale and ambition again.

From farmers to city dwellers

Historians divide the period from the beginnings of agriculture in places such as Mehrgarh (7000 BCE) to the disintegration of the Harappan Civilization (five millennia later) into four broad stages: the Early Food Producing Era (7000–5500 BCE), Regionalization or Early Harappan Era (5500–2600 BCE), Integration or Mature Harappan Era (2600–1900 BCE) and Localization or Late Harappan Era (1900–1300 BCE).

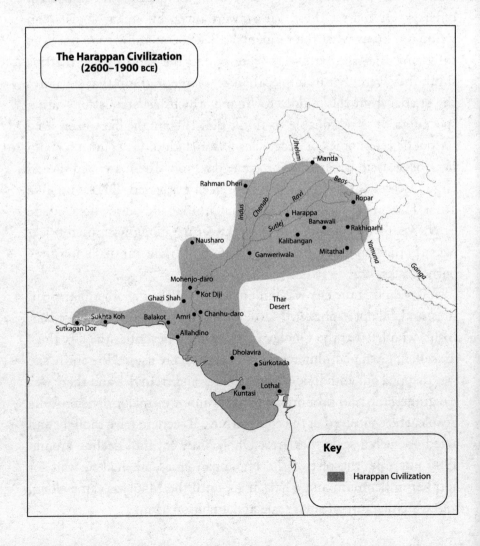

The Harappan Civilization
(2600–1900 BCE)

Manda
Rahman Dheri
Jhelum
Beas
Ropar
Indus
Chenab
Ravi
Harappa
Sutlej
Banawali
Rakhigarhi
Nausharo
Kalibangan
Ganweriwala
Mitathal
Yamuna
Ganga
Mohenjo-daro
Kot Diji
Ghazi Shah
Thar
Desert
Sukhta Koh
Balakot
Amri
Chanhu-daro
Sutkagan Dor
Allahdino
Dholavira
Surkotada
Lothal
Kuntasi

Key

Harappan Civilization

The first stage, the Early Food Producing Era, is easy enough to track. The Mehrgarh settlement lasted from around 7000 BCE to around 2600 BCE, but during this period we can see numerous other settlements springing up. The population was exploding as agriculture spread, which has happened in every part of the world that took to cultivating cereals. Some examples of new agricultural settlements are Kili Gul Mohammed in the Quetta valley, which could have begun around 5000 BCE; Damb Sadaat in Balochistan, which may go back to 3500 BCE; and Mundigak in south-eastern Afghanistan, which dates back to 4000–3500 BCE. Apart from Balochistan and nearby areas the agricultural revolution was taking place in Amri in the Indus plains in Sindh, which goes back to 3600 BCE; Rahman Dheri in Pakistan's Khyber Pakhtunkhwa province, which dates back to 3300 BCE; Kunal and Rakhigarhi in Haryana, which go back to anywhere from 4500 BCE to 3600 BCE; and Bhirrana in Haryana's Fatehabad district, which goes back even further. Many more such sites today stand as evidence that from around 7000 BCE onward the practice of agriculture was spreading rapidly in north-western India, followed by urbanization.

It would be wrong to think, though, that the population of this rapidly transforming region was formed entirely of settled farmers and city dwellers. The farmers themselves were dependent on some level of hunting and gathering still, but, more importantly, there is clear evidence of nomadic herders living in the same areas. Ratnagar says, 'Mehrgarh lies on the frontier between Sindh and Balochistan. The lower Indus plain is primarily agricultural, but over much of the broken mountain terrain of Balochistan, it is animal-herding that has prevailed over farming, which latter is confined to the narrow valleys of Balochistan . . . The Kacchi plain is a "permeable frontier" in the sense that pastoralists from the mountains around Kalat, Quetta and Loralai, who need to move their sheep from the snow-bound mountain slopes, descend on the Kacchi plain in November with their tents and animals, and sojourn amongst the local sedentary agriculturists until about February. They return to the mountains in the warmer weather.'

Even now there are many, like the Brahuis of Balochistan, who continue the pastoral tradition. Many historians believe that pastoralists were crucial participants in the emerging farming economies, both by playing a role in the exchange networks and by conveying plants and animals, new information and new inventions from one place to another, and sometimes even settling down in new areas to become farmers themselves. For many hunter-gatherers in regions far away from the two main river valleys, these nomadic herders would probably have been their first contact with a different way of living.

The next stage, the Regionalization or Early Harappan Era, is also easily graspable from the archaeological records. This is when, as the burgeoning population kept expanding into new areas, regional differences in style and culture began to become evident. Some of the bigger settlements of this period, such as Kalibangan, Banawali and Rahman Dheri, were fortified. The cultural differences were most visible in the pottery styles bearing names such as Hakra, Ravi, Balakot, Amri, Kot Diji, Nal and Sothi. An amateur may perhaps not notice the differences between these pottery types, but an archaeologist will be able to pick them out and classify them even from a jumbled pile.

The most fascinating stage to enquire into, however, is the transition to the Integration Period or the Mature Harappan Era. This is when we see many Harappan sites being newly built or rebuilt and many existing sites being abandoned, thus indicating a major realignment of population and settlements. This is also when we see a higher level of standardization, with a common script, seals, motifs and weights, spreading across the region. Overseas trade with west Asia gained significant momentum during this period as well. 'In the Mature Harappan period, local or regional culture traditions lost their distinctiveness as the metropolitan material culture engulfed the regions,' writes Ratnagar in *Understanding Harappa*.

In *A History of Ancient and Early Medieval India,* Upinder Singh points out that many Mature Harappan sites had no Early Harappan level, while many early Harappan sites had no Mature Harappan levels. And some of the sites that had both Early Harappan and Mature Harappan levels had some suggestion of an upheaval during the transition – Kot Diji, Gumla, Amri and Nausharo, for instance, had evidence of a major fire or burning between the two levels.

In short, it is difficult to escape the conclusion that the transition to the Mature Harappan Era – which archaeologists say happened over a period of four or five generations or 100 to 150 years – could not have happened without a central authority of some kind making decisions that were applied and accepted across the region, by persuasion or otherwise.

The Uruk example

We have a pretty clear idea of what happened during a similar transition at Uruk in Lower Mesopotamia because of the extensive excavations over decades that have thrown up written records relating to administrative and legal matters. In *Uruk: The First City* Liverani dissects the process in detail.

According to him, it was the need for coordinated group action to create irrigation in southern Lower Mesopotamia that ultimately led to urbanization. The irrigation system was needed because of the specific geography of southern Lower Mesopotamia, as opposed to northern Lower Mesopotamia. The northern region was a valley with narrow fields on both sides of the river, while the southern region was a delta, with broad fields on either side of the river. Irrigation in the valley did not require anything more than occasional 'submersion' of the fields from the overflow of the river, something that could be managed by a single family. In the delta, on the other hand, there was a huge opportunity to increase production by creating irrigation canals that took the water from the river to deeper inside, which required coordinated action by groups of people.

Liverani says, 'The long fields therefore required the presence of a central coordinating agency for their planning and management. Once installed, they allowed productivity on a large scale, and they were connected to other innovations.' These innovations include the seeder plough pulled by two or more pairs of oxen that ploughed the field and also sowed the seeds, and the threshing sledge pulled by an ass. Liverani estimates that canal irrigation combined with the use of animal traction would have increased the production of barley, the main crop, by five to ten times, assuming no change in the number of people employed.

During this period of unprecedented plenty, austerity and equality in society, as depicted by the house sizes and burial practices, remained unchanged. But something else did change: the size of the temples. To quote Liverani:

The moment of the enormous increase in the size of temples and their absolute predominance, when compared to domestic dwellings, corresponds clearly to the transition from the chiefdom to the early state. It is thus in the temple that we must look for the institutional organism that gave rise to the transformation. Its growth is the critical factor, the true structural change that transformed the settlements of Lower Mesopotamia from egalitarian communities to complex organisms . . .

The extraction of resources from the producers, and from consumption within the families, and their diversion towards social services, required a strong dose of coercion. Such coercion could be physical, but the use of force is expensive and becomes counterproductive after a while. Therefore, preferably the coercion is ideological. The temple was the only institution that could convince producers to give up substantial parts of their work for the advantage of the community and its administrators . . .

The temple, or 'the house of god', as it was called, was now the predominant actor in Uruk, the central agency, in terms of owning a lot of the land, and with the ability to call upon the village communities and family units to provide it almost free labour in return for subsistence food. The 'servants of god' who managed the temple and its affairs thus extracted the productive surplus in this new era of plenty and decided how it was to be allocated. This surplus thus accumulated allowed, among other things, the maintenance of an administrative machinery, including accountants who kept track of who was paid how much and owed how much in return; specialist craftsmen; and a long-distance trading system that would bring to Uruk the things it lacked: metals, wood and precious stones.

We have a reasonably good idea of the religious ideology that kept the new societal structure in place. If the farming communities, entirely dependent on their crops and herds, were singularly obsessed with fertility gods and goddesses, the newly emerging urban society felt the need for many more specialist gods and goddesses, each with expertise in a different domain but working well together. The existing ideas of sacrifices and offerings to gods continued into the urban period, with the village communities perhaps seeing the labour they provided to the temple authorities as a form of offering to the gods. 'Debate poems' were popular, and showcased arguments between the herder and the farmer, ewe and wheat, summer and winter – all trying to portray the benefits of working together and instilling the wisdom that everything had its right place and role. One myth in particular is very interesting – the myth of Atramhasis. It says that humanity was created to replace the minor gods who were tired of their hard work of farming so that the great gods could be kept well provided for.

Key questions

There are no clear parallels between the evolution of the Harappan Civilization and the Mesopotamian Civilization, but what happened in

Uruk perhaps gives one a set of good questions to pursue. For example, was there a period of dramatic agricultural productivity increase in the lead-up to the Mature Harappan period? It is indeed possible that the spread of agriculture from the mountainous valleys of Balochistan to the fertile alluvial plains of the Indus and Ghaggar–Hakra river systems led to a period of significant productivity gains. However, unlike in Uruk, there has been no evidence so far of large-scale canal irrigation in the Harappan Civilization that could have given rise to the emergence of a central agency to coordinate the work of large groups of people.

Perhaps canal irrigation was not necessary in the Indus or Ghaggar–Hakra valleys. Archaeologists believe that the irrigation was done mainly through overbank flooding due to snowmelt or monsoon, with farmers also relying on oxbow lakes (U-shaped lakes) formed during such flooding for irrigation during the dry season. So if large-scale irrigation was not the reason for the emergence of a coordinating central agency and of new power centres, could it have been the need for managing the flood or an environmental challenge of some kind? The close attention paid to water and to civic amenities and the fact that the earliest cities of the Mature Harappan phase, Harappa and Mohenjo-daro, were built on higher ground and that even now they remain unaffected during the frequent floods on the Indus – such as the one that occurred in 2010 – suggest that this is a possibility. But until archaeology or the Indus script reveals more, this will have to remain unanswered.

What about the ideology, or religion, of the Harappan Civilization that gave legitimacy to the new coordinating agency or authority structure? We do know that there are no identifiable temples within the Harappan Civilization, but that is not to say there was no religious ideology, or myths or fables that supported the power structure. Also, we might have clichéd notions about what a temple, or a palace, should look like. As Ratnagar points out, if you saw the low-slung Padmanabhapuram Palace (of the erstwhile kingdom of Travancore, now in the Kanyakumari district of Tamil Nadu), you are unlikely to identify it as one. Second, there are enough indications from seals that there were shared ideological belief systems that underpinned the Harappan Civilization.

For example, the commonest seal in the Harappan Civilization – about 60 per cent of all seals ever recovered – has the image of a unicorn. While some believe it was a 'state symbol' then, much like the Ashoka Chakra is today, others consider it the emblem of one of the constituent elements of the Harappan elite, the most common assumption about the civilization being that it had a 'ruling elite' who shared power, rather than a solitary king or an emperor. The unicorn is often found with its head above an object that has been variously described as a brazier (a container for burning coal or wood), a filter for making some kind of ritual intoxicant and a manger (the vessel

Granger Historical Picture Archive / Alamy Stock Photo

A seal depicting a unicorn standing in front of what has been variously described as a brazier, a filter and a manger

from which cattle and horses are fed). So it is obvious that there was an important mythology of some kind associated with the unicorn, though it has not survived into modern times in any recognizable form and we have no clue what it could have been.

But there are other seals that are easier to decipher. For example, there are recurring images of what looks like a deity in a peepul tree, with a kneeling worshipper in front of it. Since peepul is still

A seal from Mohenjo-daro depicting a deity wearing bangles and a horned headdress in a peepul tree, with a worshipper kneeling in front of it. Behind the worshipper is an enormous ram. At the bottom of the seal there are seven figures in procession.

Islamabad Museum

considered sacred, this should cause no surprise. There is also the figure of a 'horned deity' that appears at several Harappan sites around the beginning of the Mature Harappan period, with what looks like a buffalo-horn headdress.

Since horned figures are divinities in the Mesopotamian Civilization, some believe that this could be a shared motif. A few seals have a horned figure sitting in a striking yoga-like pose on a stool of some kind, indicating that if this was not a divinity it must at least have been a very important figure in the civilization. Another seal shows a person sitting in a tree, perhaps talking to a tiger that is turning its head to look at him. One seal shows a hero placing his foot on the horns of a water buffalo while spearing it, in front of an erect cobra.

It is clear that seals depict scenes that are evocative of religious beliefs or myths or stories that were well known to the Harappans. What these were is, of course, beyond our ken today, though we can

Angelo Hornak / Corbis / Getty Images

A horned figure sitting in a yoga-like pose

Archaeological Museum, Harappa

A seal showing a man spearing a water buffalo while placing his foot
on its head. Looking on is a seated figure wearing a horned headdress.
This seal is different from a similar one described in the text in which
a cobra is witnessing the spearing of the buffalo.

clearly see that some concepts did pass on to later periods – from the
sacredness of the peepul tree to the yoga-like pose.

The language of the Harappans

One question is key to tracing the formation of Indian populations:
what language did the Harappans speak? Most historians argue that
many languages would have been spoken in the vast region of the
civilization, not just one. Considering how many languages are spoken
in the region today – from Baluchi, Pashto, Punjabi and Gujarati to
Hindi, Brahui, Sindhi and Burushaski – this is not an unreasonable
surmise.

However, it is still possible that the civilization had one predominant
language family with its own dialects or subgroups. It is also likely that
it had an official language that was depicted in the seals. How do we
know that? When a script is used for writing different languages, the

order in which the signs/letters appear usually changes in a noticeable manner. For example, in the Harappan seals that were found in Mesopotamia or the Gulf region, experts have found that the pattern or order in which the signs appear is different from the way they appear on seals found in the Harappan Civilization itself, suggesting that in the seals found abroad the Harappan script may have been used to write a different language, perhaps Akkadian or Sumerian or other languages spoken in the Gulf region. There are no such differences in sign patterns among seals found in the Harappan Civilization region itself. Therefore, it is likely that at least during the Mature Harappan period, when there was a high degree of standardization in general, there was one language that was predominantly used, perhaps for administrative, trade and legal purposes.

So what language could this be? This would be an easy question to answer once the Harappan script is deciphered. But a century of sustained and determined efforts by a wide variety of experts from all over the world have failed to crack the script. This is not necessarily surprising because the hieroglyphic script of Egypt may not have been deciphered at all had people not stumbled upon an inscription that used multiple scripts to say the same thing. In 1799 French soldiers rebuilding a fort in Egypt discovered a stone with carvings on it in a town called Rosetta in the Nile valley. This came to be called the Rosetta Stone, and it was found to have been carved in 196 BCE by a group of priests in Egypt to honour the then pharaoh, by listing all the things he had done for the people. (Propaganda, obviously, has very ancient beginnings!)

Remarkably, the Rosetta Stone had inscriptions in three scripts, all of them in use in Egypt when the stone was carved. The first was hieroglyphic, which was used for important religious documents. The second was demotic, which was then the common script of Egypt. And the third was Greek, the language of the rulers of Egypt at that time. Shortly thereafter the hieroglyphic script was deciphered by the French scholar and philologist Jean-François Champollion, who could read

Greek and Coptic (a language that shares much with Demotic). Thus a script that had resisted all attempts at decipherment for centuries was finally decoded within a couple of decades of the discovery of the Rosetta Stone.

The story is similar in the case of the cuneiform script in which many Mesopotamian languages were written, including Sumerian, Akkadian and Elamite. Here too, it was the discovery of a multilingual inscription at Mount Behistun in the Kermanshah province of Iran that led to the final decipherment. The Behistun inscription was authored by Darius I, the fourth king of the Persian Achaemenid empire, sometime between 522 BCE and 486 BCE, and is an account of the king's life, battles and victories. The inscription had the same text in three different languages written using the same cuneiform script: Old Persian, Elamite and Akkadian. For the Harappan language, however, we have not yet found an equivalent of the Rosetta Stone or the Behistun inscription and until we do, cracking the code might prove to be difficult.

Historians and archaeologists have so far overwhelmingly backed the idea that the language underlying the Harappan script was Proto-Dravidian, but the inability to break the code has left the question hanging, without a final resolution. The debate over what language the Harappans spoke has resembled a Gordian knot more than anything else – until now.

The Gordian knot is now being cut, not because the script is closer to being deciphered, but because ancient DNA findings have now joined hands with archaeology and linguistics to provide a consistent and coherent explanation for the demographic composition and the language of the Harappans. The crucial thing to keep in mind is that these three disciplines are independent of each other, with different starting points. They also use very different materials, methodologies and scientific techniques to arrive at their conclusions. Thus it is remarkable that they all arrive at the same conclusion.

Genetic and archaeological evidence

We saw in chapter 2 how new ancient DNA evidence from west Asian and the 'Indus Periphery' individuals showed that an Iranian agriculturist population from around the Zagros region had contributed significantly to the populations in India today. This discovery rested on two sets of ancient DNA evidence – let's recount them briefly.

The first set of ancient DNA evidence was from the Zagros region of Iran dated to between 8000 BCE and 7000 BCE. It showed that these Zagrosians had a distinct type of west Eurasian ancestry. What differentiated them from others of the region was that they lacked the early Anatolian ancestry that the rest of them had.

The second set of evidence was ancient DNA from three 'Indus Periphery' outlier individuals with a unique genetic composition. Between 14 and 42 per cent of their ancestry related to First Indians, and the rest to Iranian agriculturists, and none of them had any Anatolian ancestry. This was quite unlike others around them in the same region, who all had Anatolian ancestry and no ancestry related to the First Indians.

'The Genomic Formation of South and Central Asia' study, therefore, arrived at the inescapable conclusion that these three ancient individuals were recent migrants from the Harappan Civilization; that they represent the genetic composition of the population of the Harappan Civilization itself; and that they are a mixture of Iranian agriculturists from the Zagros region and descendants of the First Indians. The scientists also concluded that the admixture between the two populations had taken place at the latest between 4700 BCE and 3000 BCE.

Please note that at no stage of this genetic trail was any reliance made on archaeological or linguistic discoveries.

No less emphatic than the genetic evidence is the archaeological evidence. In chapter 2, we saw extensive confirmation of a connection between the Zagros region and the early farmers of Mehrgarh in Balochistan. From quadrangular houses built with narrow bricks about sixty centimetres long to circular firepits filled with burnt pebbles and sequential slab construction of pottery, the similarities were striking.

To quote Jarrige:

> In spite of some obvious differences . . . the full setting of the farming economy at Mehrgarh displays evident similarities with what had been noticed in the case of the early Neolithic settlements in the hilly regions forming the eastern border of Mesopotamia [that is, the Zagros mountains of Iran] . . .
>
> The similarities noticed between Neolithic sites from the eastern border of Mesopotamia to the western margins of the Indus Valley are significant . . . A sort of cultural continuum between sites sharing a rather similar geographical context marked with an also rather similar pattern of evolution and transformation becomes more and more evident.

In other words, archaeological evidence comes to the same conclusion as ancient DNA evidence: there is a strong connection between the Zagrosians and the people of the Harappan Civilization region, dating back to a period when agriculture was only beginning in Mehrgarh. This now brings us to the third and equally important evidence linking the two regions: language.

Proto-Zagrosian and Proto-Dravidian

What languages did the west Asians speak? We can confidently answer this question only from the time when languages were written down, beginning sometime after 3500 BCE. Many Mesopotamian languages were written in the cuneiform script, until it fell into disuse in the early centuries of the Common Era. The languages that were written down using cuneiform include isolates such as Sumerian, Elamite, Hattic, Hurrian and Urartian; Semitic languages such as Akkadian, Eblaite and Armorite; and the Indo-European languages Hittite and Luwian. All these languages became extinct long ago and are not spoken anywhere today (note that the phrase Mesopotamian Civilization covers multiple kingdoms, city states and empires over thousands of years, not just one kingdom or empire).

The ancient DNA study said that the Zagrosian population and the subcontinent's First Indians had to have mixed at least by between 4700 BCE and 3000 BCE. The study did not mention the earliest possible date for the admixture. But we know that the Mehrgarh settlement, with its close connections to people from the eastern border of Mesopotamia, began around 7000 BCE. So if we are to arrive at a period of the migration, or the arrival of the Zagrosian people in south Asia, it would be sometime between 7000 BCE and 3000 BCE. So which of the Mesopotamian languages listed above are they likely to have brought to south Asia?

A serious candidate for this would be Elamite, the language of a people who built one of the most powerful and intermittently persistent kingdoms in the area covering central and southern Zagros mountains, as also the plains of Khuzistan and the Persian Gulf coast in today's Iran. The first Elamite kingdom came into being sometime around 2700 BCE, but as we have seen, the migrations from Zagros to south Asia happened much earlier. The migrants, therefore, could not have been products of the urban civilization of Elam – they preceded it. They may have spoken a Proto-Elamite language. Depending on the period of their migration, it is also possible that they were not full-fledged agriculturists yet, but herders who may, nonetheless, have had some exposure to the newly emerging culture of farming.

As we saw in chapter 2, the earliest evidence for domestication of goats comes from Ganj Dareh in the central Zagros mountains of Mesopotamia, from around 7900 BCE (the same archaeological site from where the ancient DNA was collected for the genetic study). We also saw that Mesopotamians had started migrating with their animals or goats even before the full agricultural package – cultivation of barley and wheat along with some lentils and raising sheep, goats and cattle – had become common in the region. Therefore, it is quite possible that the group of Proto-Elamite-speaking people from the south or central Zagros region who migrated to Balochistan and the surrounding areas such as Mehrgarh may have been herders with some exposure to the newly emerging practice of farming.

Some of these Zagrosian migrants who reached south Asia may have remained herders to this day, like the Brahuis of Balochistan. They speak the Brahui language, which has been linguistically determined to be closely connected to Elamite. Other migrants from the Zagros may have settled down in places like Mehrgarh to become farmers, and both the herders and the farmers may have mixed with the existing population – the First Indians – at some point. The First Indians themselves had started experimenting with agriculture in places like Lahuradewa in the Middle Ganga plain by then as we saw earlier and they may have been doing so in Balochistan as well.

So the best guess we can make based on archaeological and genetic evidence is that a population of herders from the southern or central Zagros region, speakers of Proto-Elamite or a related language, migrated to south Asia sometime after 7000 BCE, mixed with the First Indians and this new, mixed population sparked an agricultural revolution in the north-western region of India and then went on to create the Harappan Civilization over the next few millennia.

If this reconstruction of history based on archaeology and genetics is correct, then Proto-Elamite must have left a significant mark on the linguistic history of the subcontinent. Could it be Brahui with its proven links to Elamite? To some extent, yes. But considering the geographical size and demographic weight of the Harappan Civilization, there should be a much larger footprint. Could there be one? Yes, there could be: Dravidian languages, spoken by nearly a fifth of the population of India. Somewhere between 250 million and 300 million people speak a Dravidian language in the world today, making it one of the top six language families. So to this we turn now: linguistic research that shows the close connection between the Dravidian languages of India and Elamite.

A paper published in 2013 titled 'South Asia: Dravidian Linguistic History', authored by two linguists who have specialized in Dravidian languages, Professor Franklin C. Southworth and Dr David W. McAlpin, is a good place to start. McAlpin had earlier reconstructed[3] the vocabulary of Proto-Dravidian (PD), the ancient language from which all Dravidian languages – not just Tamil, Malayalam, Kannada and Telugu, but also languages such as Gondi and several others – descend, and the 2013 study uses this early vocabulary to make deductions about where and when the language may have been spoken. This is how the paper's section on PD begins:

> The reconstructed vocabulary of PD reflects a society engaged in animal husbandry, with some knowledge of agriculture. Words for sheep, goat and cattle, all inherited from Proto-Zagrosian[4] [the parent language of Proto-Elamite], along with verbs referring to 'driving' and 'grazing' animals, words for 'herd', 'flock', 'shepherd' and several words which mean both 'house/dwelling' and 'animal/

---

[3] Linguists have found that languages change over time and that when they do they follow some rules. Some of the rules are specific to all languages while other rules are specific to a particular language family. Linguists have discovered a number of such rules that are commonly accepted. The existence of these rules enables linguists to work backwards and reconstruct a parent language if they have access to a number of its descendant languages. In the past, many such reconstructions were found to be accurate when archaeologists later discovered writings that are very close to the reconstructed words/language.

[4] According to the classification made by David W. McAlpin, Proto-Zagrosian is the ancient language of south-western Iran that split into Proto-Elamitic and Proto-Dravidian, with Proto-Elamitic splitting further into Elamite and Brahui, and Proto-Dravidian splitting into Proto-Peninsular Dravidian, and Proto-North Dravidian.

stall', indicate the importance of herding. No specific [words for] grains are reconstructible, although reconstructed agricultural terms include words for digging and digging tools, operations such as winnowing, churning, reaping, and grinding grain, along with several words meaning 'grain' or 'seed', 'chaff' and 'husk', and possibly a word for the plough. The only reconstructible food plant names are onion/ garlic, yam, and eggplant, some of which may be later borrowings into individual Dravidian languages from local sources. Thus it is unlikely that these people were sedentary farmers at this stage. Several different land types are distinguished, including low lying land, uncultivated land, and field/open space. In general, older Elamite resembles PD, younger Elamite resembles Brahui. Thus we may posit, as a starting point, that the Proto-Dravidian community probably moved from somewhere in the south of present-day Iran.

The reconstructed Proto-Dravidian vocabulary enables us to put an upper limit on when Proto-Zagrosian and Proto-Dravidian separated – not before animals such as sheep and goat were domesticated and the early forms of agriculture had begun, since the two languages share the terms for domesticated animals and also for processing grains.

Interestingly, it also puts a lower limit on the separation: not after writing was invented. The reasoning is straightforward: the word 'tal' exists in both Elamite and Proto-Dravidian, but with different meanings. In Elamite, it means 'write'; in Proto-Dravidian, it means 'push in'. In a paper McAlpin authored in 1981,[5] he explains that the original meaning of 'tal' was to 'push in', but since cuneiform writing on clay tablets involved 'pushing in', the word came to mean 'writing' in Elamite after writing was invented. The reason why Proto-Dravidian speakers retained the old meaning of 'tal' is that they separated from the Elamites before writing was invented, and therefore the word never

---

[5] David W. McAlpin, 'Proto-Elamo-Dravidian: The Evidence and Its Implications', *Transactions of the American Philosophical Society* 71(3), 1981.

acquired the meaning of writing (the word for 'writing' in Dravidian languages comes from 'drawing' or 'paint').

Since we know that the earliest evidence for goat domestication comes from Ganj Dareh in the Zagros mountains from around 7900 BCE, this becomes the upper limit for the separation. Since we also know that cuneiform writing was invented sometime before 3000 BCE, this becomes the lower limit for the separation.

Considering that these linguistic studies appeared years before the genetic evidence of a Zagrosian link to the Harappans was discovered, the close correspondence between the two disciplines on the possible chronology of migrations is striking. As we saw in chapter 2, ancient DNA study puts the latest date for admixture between the Zagros agriculturists and the Harappan Civilization at 3000 BCE – exactly the same as in the linguistic study. The genetics study does not suggest an upper limit, but archaeology has something to say on this. We know the earliest evidence for animal domestication and plant cultivation in south Asia comes from Mehrgarh and is dated to sometime around 7000 BCE – which is almost an exact fit with the chronology that linguistics suggests – especially when you take into consideration the fact that after the separation in the Zagros region estimated after 7900 BCE, it would have taken some time for the Zagrosians to reach south Asia.

What is also remarkable is how old the idea of a connection between Elamite and Dravidian languages is. It was suggested by several linguists long before anyone ever knew that such a thing as the Harappan Civilization existed.

The Harappan Civilization was discovered in the 1920s. But as early as in 1853, Edwin Norris, one of the scholars who helped decipher the Behistun inscription, was pointing out that the Elamite script did not indicate contrastive voicing and worked on the same principles as the Tamil script. Three years later, when Robert Caldwell wrote the first *Comparative Grammar of the Dravidian or South Indian Family of Languages*, he used Norris's work to put forward Elamite as the first suggested affiliation for Tamil, and discussed the connection between the two languages at length. Since then, many others have mentioned or expanded on the relationship between Elamite and Dravidian languages, including Alfredo Trombetti and I.M. Diakonoff.

But the first substantive and rigorous look at the subject was a lengthy paper written by McAlpin in 1981, titled 'Proto-Elamo-Dravidian: The Evidence and Its Implications'. This was a tour de force, though many linguists at the time were cautious in accepting it. This was not surprising since Elamite had been extinct for over two millennia and the last written Elamite records were available only from around 450 BCE. There aren't too many word roots that can be reconstructed for Proto-Elamite based on the limited supply of such old writings. Moreover, Proto-Zagrosian and Proto-Dravidian may have separated as early as 7000 BCE to 6000 BCE, going on to evolve along their own separate pathways since then. So to establish a relationship between the two languages based on reconstructed Proto-Elamite or Proto-Zagrosian was a dauntingly difficult task to begin with.

But as McAlpin says in his magisterial work, it is this very difficulty that makes the extent of similarities surprising. Out of the 250 word roots that McAlpin was able to identify for Elamite, over 40 per cent are cognate with, or similar to, Dravidian. With such a high rate of common root words which is 'emphatically above chance levels', says McAlpin, 'the basic case becomes an established prima facie one'.

Since the paper was published in 1981, the evidence has only accumulated further, and the 2013 paper by Southworth and McAlpin is evidence of that. With the new ancient DNA discovery and the existing archaeological evidence connecting the Zagros region to the agricultural beginnings in south Asia, the conclusion of McAlpin's 1981 paper now is not just compelling, but unavoidable.

Here's a sample of the kind of lexical connections that McAlpin uncovered. Needless to say, these would seem remarkable to anyone familiar with the Dravidian languages. These are ten of the eighty-one words that McAlpin has listed in his paper.

1. Proto-Elamo-Dravidian: *hiṭ- (to herd goats, goat); Achaemenid Elamite: hidu (adult female goat, goats in general); Proto-Dravidian: *iṭ- (to herd goats); Tamil: iṭai (herdsman caste); Malayalam: iṭayan (a caste of shepherds and cowherds).

2. Proto-Elamo-Dravidian: *pot (young animal); Achaemenid Elamite: putu (lamb); Proto-Dravidian: *pōt (young animal or plant); Tamil: pōttu (sapling).

3. Proto-Elamo-Dravidian: *vari- (to fix, tie, hold); Middle Elamite: mari- (to seize, grasp, capture); Proto-Dravidian: *vari- (to bind, tie, fasten); Tamil: vari (to bind, tie, fasten).

4. Proto-Elamo-Dravidian: *um- (to process grain); Achaemenid Elamite: umi- (to grind grain); Proto-Dravidian: *um (husk, chaff); Tamil: umi (husk, to become chaff); Telugu: umaka (husk, chaff).

5. Proto-Elamo-Dravidian: *ni (you); Old Elamite: ni (you); Proto-Dravidian: *nī (you). This is a basic term attested in all Dravidian languages and means exactly the same – you.

6. Proto-Elamo-Dravidian: *naḷ (day); Middle Elamite: nā, nana (days); Proto-Dravidian: *nāḷ (day).

7. Proto-Elamo-Dravidian: *tol̤- (to perforate, bore); Middle Elamite: tullin (breach, cut, slice); Proto-Dravidian: *tol̤- (to perforate, bore); Telugu: tolucu (to bore, perforate).

8. Proto-Elamo-Dravidian: *cah- (to die); Middle Elamite: sa- (his life should be cut off); Proto-Dravidian: *caH- (to die); Tamil: cā(k/v)/ce (to die, be blighted); Malayalam: cākuka/ca- (to die).

9. Proto-Elamo-Dravidian: *ul (inside, interior, mind, heart, to think); Middle Elamite: ulhi (dwelling place, residence, sanctuary); Tamil: uḷḷam (mind, thought)

10. Proto-Elamo-Dravidian: *kaṭ (bed, throne); Royal Achaemenid Elamite: kat (place, throne); Proto-Dravidian: *kaṭṭil (cot, bedstead, throne of distinction); Tamil: kaṭṭil (cot, bedstead).

Correspondences between the two languages in terms of word roots is only one part of McAlpin's work; the other and equally substantial part of his work looks at similarities in terms of morphology and other elements that go into the making of any language.

There is yet another striking piece of evidence that suggests that the Harappan language was Proto-Dravidian, but which McAlpin doesn't mention because it deals not with Elamite, but with Akkadian, one of the dominant Semitic languages of the Mesopotamian Civilization. In chapter 2 (p. 103), we saw there was one plant that was imported from the Harappan Civilization to Mesopotamia: sesame. Remarkably, the name of this oilseed is the same in Akkadian and in many Dravidian languages of south India today: ellu. Writes Professor Southworth in *Linguistic Archaeology of South Asia*, 'the sharing of a word for sesame between Mesopotamia (Akkadian ellu) and South India (South Dravidian 1: ellu) reinforces the hypothesis of the presence of Dravidian speakers in the prehistoric Indus Valley'.

What about Indo-European languages that today dominate the region that once belonged to the Harappan Civilization? Could not these languages have been spoken there during the Harappan period? We will come to that in chapter 4, but briefly, the generally accepted chronology for the spread of Indo-European languages around the world puts their arrival in south Asia only after 2000 BCE, when the Harappan Civilization was already in decline. This has been strongly supported by recent genetic studies based on ancient DNA which suggest that Steppe pastoralists, who took Indo-European languages to Europe, reached India only in the Late Harappan period, bringing with them an early version of Sanskrit and related cultural concepts and practices such as ritual sacrifices. Many of these practices and beliefs are reflected in the Vedas, especially the earliest one, the Rigveda. The newly arrived Indo-European-language speakers called themselves 'Aryans'. What all of this means is that the Harappan Civilization had nothing to do with the 'Aryans' or Sanskrit or the Vedas, and was pre-'Aryan' or pre-Vedic. We will discuss this further in the next chapter.

Deciphering the Harappan script

It is no surprise then that most of the attempts at deciphering the Harappan script have assumed that the language underlying it was Dravidian. Even though the script has not been deciphered after nearly a century of concerted attempts, the efforts of two independent experts in particular have been noteworthy: Dr Iravatham Mahadevan, the epigraphist who helped decipher the Tamil Brahmi script in which the earliest records of Dravidian are kept, and Professor Asko Parpola. Each of them brought new perspectives on how to start reading the script.

Until the script is deciphered, it cannot be used to either buttress or weaken the common conclusions being reached by archaeology, genetics and linguistics. However, it is worth quoting Mahadevan's convocation address at the Dravidian University in Kuppam, Andhra Pradesh, in 2015, for two reasons. One, his strong rebuttal of the belief that the Harappans spoke an Indo-European language and that they were Vedic Aryans. And two, his description of the direction in which the deciphering efforts are tending:

> The results I have obtained so far confirm that the language of the Indus script is an early form of Dravidian. I do not claim to have deciphered the Indus Script completely. But I sincerely believe that I have discovered important clues for interpreting many of the frequent Indus signs and sequences proving conclusively the Dravidian character of the language and the survival of the Indus elements in the twin streams of later Dravidian and Indo-Aryan traditions . . .
>
> There is substantial evidence that the Indus Civilization was pre-Aryan.
> 1. The Indus Civilization was mainly urban, while the early Vedic society was rural and pastoral. There were no cities in the Vedic period.
> 2. The Indus seals depict many animals but not the horse. The horse and the chariot with spoked wheels were the defining

features of the Aryan-speaking societies. The bronze chariot found at Daimabad in Western Deccan, the Southernmost Indus settlement, has solid wheels and is drawn by a pair of humped bulls, not horses.

3. The tiger is often featured on Indus seals and sealings, but the animal is not mentioned in the Rigveda.

Mahadevan goes on to enumerate the substantial archaeological and linguistic evidence that supports the Dravidian nature of the Harappan Civilization. The evidence includes pictorial depictions on seals and sealings that suggest the worship of a buffalo-horned male god, mother goddesses, the peepul tree, the serpent and, possibly, the phallic symbol, all of which have been derived not from the earliest Vedas, but from the pre-Aryan population. Many of these went on to become part of the Indian cultural tradition as we know it today, and this is a crucial point Mahadevan makes. 'The Indus heritage is shared by Dravidian as well as Indo-Aryan speakers. The Dravidian heritage is linguistic. The Indo-Aryan heritage is cultural, preserved through loanwords [words taken from another language], loan translations [phrases taken from another language], and myths . . . As I read it, the message of the Indus Script is: unity in diversity.'

In other words, after Indo-European-language speakers reached south Asia, the language of the Harappans became limited to south India, while the culture and myths of the Harappans melded with those of the new Indo-Aryan-language-speaking migrants to create a unique, syncretic tradition that is today seen as an essential part of Indian culture. Therefore, there is a disconnect between the earliest Vedas and the culture and practices of the Harappan Civilization, but a connect between the later Vedic corpus and the Harappan Civilization because these by then incorporate some of the ideas and themes of the Harappans. It is thus possible to see the heritage of Harappa in the language/s of the Dravidians, and in the myths, phrases and words

National Museum of India / Angelo Hornak / Corbis / Getty Images

A figurine of a woman from the Harappan Civilization.
Some see the figurine as a 'Mother Goddess'.

borrowed by the Indo-Aryans from the Harappan tradition. (See section titled 'Harappans and the Vedas: Disconnect and connect' in chapter 4 for details.)

Mahadevan identifies grammatical signs in the Harappan script that stand for the masculine singular suffix and also the non-masculine singular suffix. He identifies the arrow sign that frequently appears in the script as 'ampu' – the Dravidian word that means 'arrow', but also stands for the non-masculine singular suffix in the earliest Kannada, Tamil and Telugu inscriptions, which means it appears at the end of female names.[6] Similarly, he identifies the frequently occurring jar sign in the Harappan script as the masculine singular suffix 'anru' that is often appended at the end of male names.

Mahadevan's most striking observation about the Harappan script is that many of its signs refer to the meticulously planned Harappan cities with their grid-like streets oriented towards the four cardinal directions and fortified citadels built on a high artificial terrace. For example, he identifies the square sign with a smaller square inside it as referring to an official title, 'The Lord of the House', or 'akatti' in Dravidian, drawn from the root word 'akam', meaning inside the house/palace/fort/mind. The square itself, in this interpretation, would refer to the citadel or fort, and the small square inside it to its main resident. In Old Tamil, the word 'akatton' means 'The Lord of the Fort'. Mahadevan suggests the name Agastya comes from 'akatti' and that the legend of Agastya in Old Tamil literature – where he is thought to have led eighteen kings and eighteen families of the Velir clan from north India to south India – could refer to the rulers of the Harappan Civilization who migrated to the south after the civilization declined.

By linking many signs in the script to Harappan cities themselves, he also shows how the Cheras, Cholas and Pandiyas (three Tamil dynasties with a long history spanning centuries before and after the Common Era) may be identified by the roles they played within the Harappan urban civilization. He says: 'The Chola were counsellors "surrounding" and "advising" the Ruler. The Chera or Cheral were high officials residing in exclusive quarters (keri) with restricted entry. The Panti were the commoners who resided in the streets, "pati" of the (lower) city, "pali". These results corroborate the folklore that the

---

[6] This practice of using a pictogram to refer not to its obvious meaning, but to a word that sounds exactly similar is called 'rhebus' and is quite common among early scripts.

Chera, Chola and Panti were brothers who lived together in one place in ancient times.'

This is a fascinating interpretation, but until more of the script is deciphered, we will not know for sure whether it is accurate – even though in Egyptian hieroglyphics there are very similar signs, with rectangles rather than squares, that carry similar meanings: house and fortified house. Also, the title of the ancient Egyptian rulers, Pharaoh, literally means 'Great House'.

If Mahadevan used the Harappan city structure to decipher meanings in some of its inscriptions, Parpola turned to astronomy to find meanings in other parts. His argument is that astronomy was important and prevalent during the Harappan Civilization, just as in the Mesopotamian Civilization, especially considering the way the cities were built along cardinal directions.

Both Mahadevan and Parpola begin with the assumption that the seals are likely to bear proper names of persons, with or without their official titles, just as they did in Mesopotamian seals. About thirty Harappan seals have been recovered from the Gulf and Mesopotamia, probably left there by seafaring Indian merchants, thus proving the importance the seal played as a way of guaranteeing the true provenance of merchandise. Both Mahadevan and Parpola also think the culture that followed the decline of the Harappan Civilization, after the arrival of Indo-European-language speakers, assimilated a number of Harappan concepts and cultural practices. Therefore, they use later traditions in Dravidian languages such as Tamil and Indo-European languages such as Sanskrit to substantiate their readings of the script.

The most striking of Parpola's decipherments relates to the frequently appearing sign of the fish in the Harappan script. In Parpola's reading, the fish sign in the Harappan script refers to 'miin', the Dravidian word for both fish and star. Parpola argues that the frequency of the sign in the Harappan script – about one in ten signs is either fish or a modified fish – suggests that its most common reference is to star rather than fish.

Therefore, a sign with six vertical strokes followed by a fish could mean 'aru' plus 'miin' – with 'aru' meaning six in Dravidian, and 'miin' meaning star or fish. As it happens, there is indeed a constellation that is called 'aru-miin' – the Pleiades. There are also Harappan inscriptions that show seven vertical strokes followed by a fish – which would read as 'elu-miin' in Dravidian, meaning seven stars, which refers to the constellation Ursa Major.

According to Parpola, both the Pleiades and Ursa Major play an important role not only in early Indian mythology but also in the early history of Indian calendrical astronomy, which is probably of Harappan origin. The suggestion that the fish sign in the Harappan script could mean star predates Parpola, but he has built on the idea so extensively that he has made it impossible for anyone to ignore it.

Archaeological Survey of India

A seal depicting a unicorn. The inscription shows seven vertical strokes followed by a fish which could refer to the constellation of Ursa Major.

The route to the south

If the dominant language of the Harappans was Proto-Dravidian, when did it reach south India from north-western India? The most common assumption is that this happened after the civilization declined and new migrants speaking Indo-European languages – or Aryans – arrived in north-western India sometime after 2000 BCE. This is the event that the Agastya or Akatti legend perhaps refers to. But Agastya and his Velir clans need not have been the first to bring Dravidian languages to south India, though they may have brought a more urbane form of it.

In fact, there is reason to think Dravidian languages may have reached south India perhaps as early as around 2800 BCE, even before the Mature Harappan period began in 2600 BCE. This is around the time that we see the first evidence of pastoralism in south India, in northern Karnataka. Those who brought Dravidian languages to south India first may not have been the urbanites of the Harappan Civilization but pastoralists, some of whom may remain so even today, like the Brahuis of Balochistan. As we saw earlier, those who arrived in south Asia from the Zagros region were probably herders rather than full-fledged farmers, and while some of them settled down as farmers (perhaps after mixing with indigenous south Asians who were already experimenting with farming), others may have remained pastoralists. There is a possibility that some of these pastoralists may have brought cattle and goat herding to south India and they could have been the first to bring a Dravidian language here too.

A look at the climatic map of India will show that there is a savannah zone – an expanse covered in grasses – that runs from Gujarat and Rajasthan through the central Deccan and all the way down to south India, along the western side of the peninsula. This would have been a perfect route for pastoralists to take, as they expanded their range.

In the 2006 paper 'Agricultural Origins and Frontiers in South Asia: A Working Synthesis', the archaeobotanist Dorian Q. Fuller laid out the case for the introduction of domesticated animals – cattle, sheep and goats – into peninsular India from the north. According to him, people in peninsular India had taken to cultivating two kinds of small millets and two kinds of pulses, a basic crop package like barley and wheat in north-western India, sometime between 3000 BCE and 2300 BCE. They had domesticated these millets and pulses from locally available wild varieties. The earliest evidence for the integration of this agricultural package with domesticated animals – mainly cattle, but also sheep and goat – comes from 'ashmounds', or large mounds of ash formed by the burning of cow dung, dated from around 2200 BCE. Fuller considers this 'ashmound tradition' to be the outcome of interaction between cultivators and immigrant pastoralists, though he does not make any link between this possibility and language expansion.

In other words, the introduction of pastoralism and domesticated animals to a region and a people who were experimenting with cultivation of millets and pulses is what could have led to the development of the full package of crops and domesticated animals. If this assessment is right, it is a possibility that migrant Dravidian-language speakers could have been a crucial part of the agricultural story in southern India. The possible arrival of Harappan urbanites almost a thousand years later would have built on an existing foundation of Dravidian language presence in south India.

The distribution of Dravidian place names in Maharashtra, Gujarat and north-western India could provide further evidence in support of the spread of Dravidian languages from north-west India to south India. Professor Franklin C. Southworth did an extensive study of Maharashtrian place names in *Linguistic Archaeology of South Asia*, and he wrote:

The primary evidence for the existence of Dravidian place names in Maharashtra consists of an estimated 800 or more village names with the suffixes -vali or oli, probably derived from the Dravidian palli, a word meaning 'hamlet' or 'village' in Proto-Dravidian which occurs widely as a place-name suffix in south India. The differences in distribution between the suffixes -vali/oli and -gav (from grama, a word of Indo-European origin) suggest that different parts of Maharashtra were probably settled by Dravidian and Indo-Aryan speakers, with the Dravidian areas mainly in the Konkan (coastal region) and the southeastern part of the Deccan plateau. Apart from the fact that the regions in which these suffixes are found are contiguous with areas to the south which show the Dravidian forms of the same suffixes, the probability of Dravidian influence is supported by other place name suffixes, as well as some initial place name elements, in those same parts of Maharashtra.'

Dravidian variations of 'palli' include 'halli' in the Kannada language, which often substitutes 'h' for 'p'.
Southworth then goes on:

Place names with the suffix -vali and variants also occur in Gujarat, Sindh, East and West Panjab, Haryana, western Uttar Pradesh and Orissa (although not elsewhere in eastern India or Bangladesh), albeit with less frequency than in Maharashtra . . . Thus these regions may also have been home to speakers of Dravidian languages in the past, though it has not been possible here to investigate this wider region in the same detail as for Maharashtra . . .

The existence of Dravidian river names in northeastern Maharashtra suggests that all of Maharashtra might have been Dravidian-speaking at an earlier time . . .

Southworth doesn't rule out the possibility that the 'widespread occurrence' of Dravidian place names in coastal and south-western Maharashtra, as well as in Gujarat and elsewhere, resulted from a later movement of Dravidian speakers from south India, but says, 'Whatever may be the case, we are probably justified in concluding that by the early first millennium CE, extensive areas of Gujarat, coastal Maharashtra and southern Maharashtra were occupied by a population that used a Dravidian language for daily interaction – either as a primary home language and/or a lingua franca.'

Taking into account the archaeological, genetic and linguistic evidence for Proto-Dravidian being the lingua franca of the Harappan Civilization, a parsimonious conclusion would be that the distribution of Dravidian place names all the way from north-western India to south India indicates the movement of people from there to the south.

Austroasiatic-language speakers

So far, we have documented the arrival and expansion of two major groups that later intermixed and went on to create the Harappan Civilization and provide the foundation for the Indian population structure as we find it today: the original Out of Africa migrants (chapter 1) and herders from the Zagros region of Iran (chapters 2 and 3). We could do so because there has been substantial research – archaeological, genetic, linguistic and epigraphic – that has given us an insight into how our prehistory unfolded. But there is a third group that has contributed much to our civilization – the Austroasiatic-language speakers – but they have not been studied anywhere near as much, which means information about them is sketchy. Hopefully, this will be rectified sometime soon.

The languages Indians speak fall into four major families – Dravidian, which is spoken by about a fifth of Indians and has no relatives outside of south Asia today; Indo-European, which is spoken by over three-quarters of Indians and is spread all the way from south Asia to Europe; Austroasiatic, which is spoken by about 1.2 per cent of Indians and is spread across south Asia and east Asia; and Tibeto-Burman, which is spread across south Asia, China and south-east Asia and is spoken by less than 1 per cent of Indians. The popularity and geographical spread of different language families require a historical

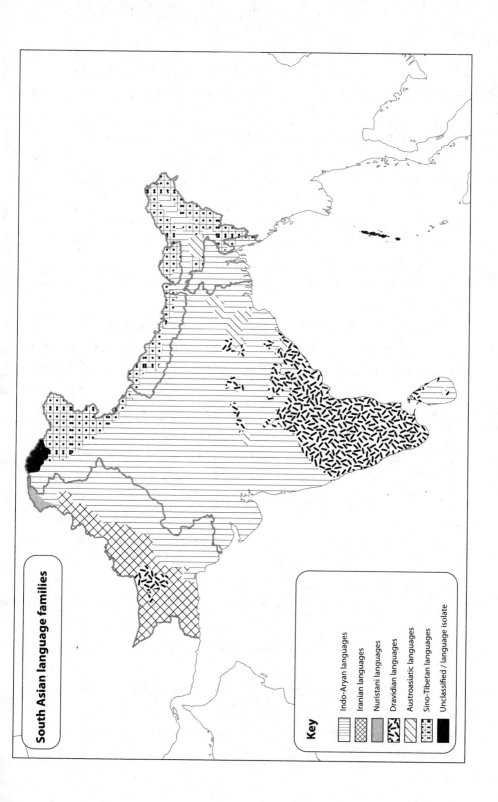

South Asian language families

Key

Indo-Aryan languages
Iranian languages
Nuristani languages
Dravidian languages
Austroasiatic languages
Sino-Tibetan languages
Unclassified / language isolate

explanation, even if we all agree that languages are not always spread by large-scale migrations. There are instances when languages are spread more by contact or elite dominance rather than large-scale migrations. The ubiquity of English in India, for example, is not evidence of the Europeans genetically or demographically overwhelming the Indians, but of a period of intense contact between Europeans and Indians, resulting in the continuing popularity of English.

We have already seen the prehistory of Dravidian languages in south Asia, so in this section we will look at how Austroasiatic languages and Tibeto-Burman came to be distributed the way they are. There is more evidence about the prehistory of Austroasiatic languages than about Tibeto-Burman, so let's look at that first.

In India, Austroasiatic languages belong to two subfamilies: Munda and Khasi. Munda languages such as Mundari, Santali and Ho are today spoken mostly in parts of eastern India (mainly Jharkhand) and also central India, with the westernmost language being Korku spoken in Madhya Pradesh and Maharashtra. Khasi, on the other hand, is spoken primarily in Meghalaya and to some extent in Assam. As part of the Austroasiatic language family, both Munda and Khasi are related to the Mon-Khmer languages of Vietnam, Cambodia and parts of Nepal, Burma, Bangladesh, Malaysia, Thailand, Laos and southern China. There are altogether about 104 million people who speak one version or the other of the Austroasiatic language, which makes it the eighth largest language family in the world. Nicobarese, spoken in the Andaman and Nicobar Islands, is also an Austroasiatic language.

There are two questions related to the origin and spread of Austroasiatic languages in India that have long been debated. One, did these languages originate in India and then spread to south-east Asia and farther, or did they migrate from south-east Asia to India? Two, if they did migrate to India from south-east Asia, did they bring the practice of rice farming with them?

Two recently published genetic studies have provided answers to both these questions: one based on ancient DNA that looked at how south-east Asia was populated, and the other that looked at the origins of Asian cultivated rice. The first study was published as recently as in March 2018 and the second one was published a month later. A third paper, published in 2011, that looked at the population genetic structure of Indian Austroasiatic-language speakers had also addressed one of these questions. So first, the migration question: did Austroasiatic-language speakers migrate to south Asia from east Asia? A recently published paper that answers this question, even if indirectly, is titled 'Ancient Genomics Reveals Four Prehistoric Migrations into South-East Asia'. It was supported by twenty-six institutes and universities from Southeast Asia and around the world and lead-authored by scientists from the Centre for GeoGenetics, Natural History Museum of Denmark. The study had access to ancient DNA samples from Malaysia, Thailand, the Philippines, Vietnam, Indonesia and Laos, dating to between 8000 and 200 years ago.

The study found that within the last 4000 years or so, south-east Asia saw dramatic changes in its demography as a result of at least two major waves of migration with their origin in China after it had gone through an agricultural revolution. Rice and millets had been fully domesticated in the Yangtze and Yellow river valleys of China between 7500 BCE and 3500 BCE and there is evidence for paddy fields by around 2500 BCE. There were two separate migrations of these farming populations – one through an inland route which accounts for the spread of Austroasiatic languages in south-east Asia, and the other through an island-hopping route, accounting for the spread of the Austronesian group of languages in maritime south-east Asia (including Malaysia, Indonesia and the Philippines) and the islands of the Pacific Ocean and Madagascar. India has no presence of Austronesian languages, so it is the first wave of migration through the land route, dated to around 2000 BCE, that is of direct relevance to our story.

The study says these migrations that brought agriculture to south-east Asia caused a 'dramatic change in ancestry' there, with the original hunter-gatherers of the region – who are called Hoabinhian and are related to the Onge of the Andamans – being displaced by Austroasiatic-language-speaking agriculturists. The study had no access to ancient DNA of Austroasiatic-language speakers from India and so it makes no conclusions about their ancestry. However, since the study shows the connection between the Austroasiatic-language-speaking farmers of south-east Asia and the inland migration wave originating from China, the idea that Austroasiatic-language speakers may have spread from India to south-east Asia becomes untenable. The short explanation for the presence of Austroasiatic-language speakers in India, therefore, is that they arrived from south-east Asia around or after 2000 BCE, as part of the farming migrations originating from China.

This suggests that around the time the Harappan Civilization was beginning to crumble in north-western India, there was an influx of people coming through eastern India.

This is not surprising because an earlier study published in 2011, titled 'Population Genetic Structure in Indian Austroasiatic Speakers', had arrived at similar findings. This study was based on present-day genetic samples from forty-five Indians and fifteen Burmese covering three major language groups – Austroasiatic, Dravidian and Tibeto-Burman – and was co-authored by Gyaneshwer Chaubey, Toomas Kivisild and Mait Metspalu, among others. Its conclusion was clear: 'We propose that Austroasiatic speakers in India today are derived from dispersal from southeast Asia, followed by extensive sex-specific admixture with local Indian populations.'

The study found a 'significant southeast Asian component' (about 25 per cent) among Indian Munda speakers. The strongest signal of south-east Asian genetic ancestry among Indian Austroasiatic speakers, says the study, is seen in their Y-chromosome, 'with approximately two-thirds falling into haplogroup O2a'. This haplogroup is older and has significantly higher diversity in south-east Asia, strongly suggesting that it travelled from there to India rather than the other way around. The study also found that the south-east Asian ancestry signal has been 'entirely lost' in the mtDNA lineages of Munda speakers, which means that their maternal lineages are of Indian origin.

This takes us to the second question: did the Austroasiatic-language speakers bring rice farming to India? The short answer is no, and the long answer we will come to in a while. The study that answered the question conclusively was published in April 2018 and was titled 'Genomic Variation in 3010 Accessions of Asian Cultivated Rice'. This exhaustive research into the history of rice farming in Asia was led by the Crop Science Institute of the Chinese Academy of Agricultural Sciences and the International Institute of Rice Research, and the conclusion it came to was unequivocal: Asian rice (or *Oryza sativa*), which has two major subspecies called indica and japonica, had multiple independent domestications. This is how the study (which uses the name XI for indica rice) puts it: 'Taken together, our results – combined with archaeological evidence of XI cultivation for over 9000 years in both India and China – support multiple independent domestications of *Oryza sativa*.' As we saw in the previous chapter, there was evidence for harvesting of rice at Lahuradewa in the Sant Kabir Nagar district of Uttar Pradesh, dating back to 7000 BCE, and this study now provides additional evidence and puts the issue of origins of rice cultivation to rest.

But there is a longer story too. The rice that was harvested in Lahuradewa and later domesticated in India is the indica subspecies of *Oryza sativa*, while the subspecies that was domesticated in the Yangtze valley of China is japonica. The unlocking of the full potential of rice cultivation in India might have required hybridization of indica with japonica.

According to Fuller, the protracted domestication process of rice in India was completed around 4000 years ago, 'when hybridization with Chinese rice took place'.[7] Another study published in 2017, titled

---

[7] Dorian Q. Fuller, 'Pathways to Asian Civilizations: Tracing the Origin and Spread of Rice and Rice Cultures', Rice (2011).

'Approaching Rice Domestication in South Asia: New Evidence from Indus Settlements in Northern India', also came to a similar conclusion: 'The data also suggest that when fully domesticated *Oryza Sativa* ssp [subspecies] japonica was introduced around 2000 BCE, it arrived in an area already familiar with rice cultivation and a range of cultivation techniques.'

So the emerging picture is of a productivity boost that occurs when japonica arrives in an area already familiar with rice agriculture and its hybridization with indica takes place. It is noteworthy that the period when this happened – around 2000 BCE – is the same as the period of arrival of Austroasiatic-language speakers from south-east Asia. Fuller, however, believes the introduction of japonica could have happened through the north-west region of India via trade rather than the north-east via migrations.

Fuller's reason for not supporting the eastern India migration route for the introduction of japonica into India is that there is no archaeological or achaeobotanical evidence for it. However, he himself says there could be a valid reason for such lack of evidence: 'Admittedly, Burma, Assam, Yunnan and Bengal are among the least well-known regions archaeobotanically and archaeologically – archaeology is very geographically biased.' Fuller's article was also written before there was ancient DNA evidence linking a migration from China around 2000 BCE to the spread of farming and Austroasiatic languages in south-east Asia.

Taking the DNA evidence into account, and the arrival of many east Asian crops and practices into India around 2000 BCE, a parsimonious explanation might be that starting around 2000 BCE there was increasing contact between the Indian and Chinese civilizations, through both trade and migrations and through both the eastern and north-western regions. And this could have involved the migrations of not just Austroasiatic-language speakers, but also Tibeto-Burman-language speakers. Unlike in the case of Austroasiatic-language speakers, there has never been a debate about the east Asian origins of Tibeto-Burman language (part of the larger Sino-Tibetan language family) speakers, who are today spread in small pockets in the Himalayan and sub-Himalayan regions and number about 5.5 million. This family includes the Meitei language of Manipur and the Tani languages of Arunachal Pradesh.

Here's a partial list of crops that Fuller says did come through the north-eastern part of India, via Assam to the Indian plains: citrus trees, cultivated mango and the fibre crop ramie (*Boehmeria nivea*). The Mundas who preferred the hills to the plains, according to Fuller, are likely to have brought with them taro and a variety of rice called aus rather than japonica.

Whichever way you look at it, by around 2000 BCE, some of the most important elements that make up India's population as it is today were in place: the descendants of the Out of Africa migrants, the Zagros agriculturists, the Austroasiatic-language speakers and the Tibeto-Burman-language speakers. The wheels of history were turning, making a unique culture out of many different traditions, practices and belief systems. But there was one component yet missing: those who called themselves 'Aryans'. To them, we turn now.

Note on the name: What is the correct name to call the earliest Indian civilization? Should one call it the Harappan Civilization, the Indus Valley Civilization, the Indus–Sarasvati Civilization or the Sarasvati Civilization? In this book, we have followed the style of naming a civilization by the first city that was discovered. Harappa was the first city of the ancient Indian civilization to be discovered in the 1920s, and hence it came to be called the Harappan Civilization early on. The term 'Indus Valley Civilization' is not correct because what it seeks to describe ranges far beyond the Indus Valley itself. The same objection applies to the name 'Sarasvati Valley'. The Indus–Sarasvati Valley Civilization may be a more accurate name than either Indus Valley or Sarasvati Valley, but the naming of Ghaggar–Hakra as Sarasvati is not without controversy and, in any case, the name does not cover all parts of the civilization – Dholavira and Lothal are neither in the Indus Valley nor in the Sarasvati Valley. For these reasons, this book sticks to the name Harappan Civilization.

4

The Last Migrants: The 'Aryans'

How a band of warriors and pastoralists from the Steppe first dominated Europe and then south Asia, giving India its largest family of languages, new religious customs and a cultural mix that combined Harappan traditions and Steppe practices.

There is no question in Indian prehistory that has caused more heat and dust than this one: 'when and how did Indo-European-language speakers, who called themselves Aryans, reach the Indian subcontinent?'

This is curious because no similar and extreme controversy surrounds questions like 'when did the first inhabitants reach India?' or 'when did Dravidian-language speakers reach India?' or 'when did the Mundari, Khasi or Meitei-language speakers reach India?' It provokes no one's ire when it is said that the original inhabitants of India came from Africa; that Proto-Dravidian is related to the Elamitic language of Iran; or that Mundari, Khasi and Meitei speakers came from east Asia. All of this is taken with a shrug because, after all, there is no nation in the world today that has not been shaped by repeated mass migrations. Europe has seen its demography upturned at least two times through mass migrations. The Americas saw at least three major migrations that shaped their demography and these were even before the first European set foot there. East Asia has seen at least three major migrations, while central Asia and west Asia have been the sites of so many invasions and migrations that it is difficult to keep count.

And it is not as if Indians have not ventured out and influenced other regions massively either, especially in the early centuries of the Common Era. All of south-east Asia, from today's Vietnam and Cambodia to Burma, Thailand and Indonesia, once fell within the ambit of India's cultural pre-eminence. Even China came under the spell of India for a while. Occasionally this may have involved invasion, but more often it involved the ceaseless efforts of Buddhist missionaries keen to spread their religion, and very often it had to do with merchants out to make a profit and protect and further their interests. That Buddhism has 488 million adherents around the world, with only a minority of them in India today, is testimony to the impact India made outside of its natural boundaries.

So what accounts for this special sensitivity to the question about the arrival of Indo-European-language speakers? The answer is simple: it is the unstated but underlying assumption that Indian culture is identical or synonymous with 'Aryan', 'Sanskrit' or 'Vedic' culture. Therefore, to ask when Indo-European languages reached India would be seen to be the same as asking, 'when did we import our culture?'

But this is ridiculous on two counts. First of all, Indian culture is not synonymous with, or identical to, 'Aryan' or 'Sanskrit' or 'Vedic' culture. 'Aryan' culture was an important stream that contributed to creating the unique Indian civilization as we know it today, but by no means was it the only one. There were other streams that have contributed equally to making Indian civilization what it is. Second, to say that Indo-European languages reached India at a particular historical juncture is not the same as suggesting that the 'Vedas' or 'Sanskrit' or the 'Aryan' culture was imported flat-packed and then reassembled here. 'Aryan' culture was most likely the result of interaction, adoption and adaptation among those who brought Indo-

European languages to India and those who were already well-settled inhabitants of the region.

So to come back to the question: did Indo-European-language speakers, who called themselves Aryans, come from elsewhere, and if they did, when did they do so?

Out of India is out of the reckoning

Until recently, there was some room for debate on the question whether the spread of Indo-European languages around the world could be explained by people moving out of India with an early version of Sanskrit rather than people moving into India with an early version of Sanskrit. But genetic studies, especially those based on ancient DNA, are rapidly closing the door on that debate. Here is how they are doing it.

About three-quarters of Indians today speak an Indo-European language such as Hindi, Gujarati, Bengali, Punjabi or Marathi. So does about 40 per cent of the world, with Spanish, English, French, Portuguese, Iranian, Russian and German being some of the other widely spoken Indo-European languages. The Indian subcontinent forms the easternmost limit of the Indo-European language family range, there being no large populations speaking any Indo-European languages to our east. So the natural question arises: how did this language family become the dominant language in India? There are only two possible answers: either it came to India from the outside sometime in the past, or it went from India to the rest of the world that is west of it.

Let us consider the second possibility first: that a large number of Sanskrit- or Proto-Sanskrit-speaking Indians once ventured west and they and their descendants spread out over vast regions all the way from Iran to central Asia to west Asia to eastern Europe and western Europe, thus spawning versions of Indo-European languages along the route. What would you then expect to see in the genetic record of all those regions? A fair sprinkling of the genetic signature of the

First Indians, the descendants of the Out of Africa migrants. As we saw in the previous chapters, the first migrants had spread all over the subcontinent and were part of the population that built the Harappan Civilization as well. So if significant emigrations from India any time before or after the Harappan Civilization were responsible for the spread of Indo-European languages, we would have to see their genetic footprints all the way from central Asia to western Europe. Is there such a large signature across this region? No. On the contrary, as we saw in chapter 1, the descendants of the First Indians have no close relatives anywhere else in the world. So the idea of an Out of India migration that spread Indo-European languages around the world is a non-starter.

There is one exception to this that proves the rule – the Roma, a relatively small itinerant ethnic group living mostly in Europe and the Americas who were earlier known as Gypsies. Genetic studies have confirmed that they come from a single ethnic group that left north-western India (the regions of Punjab, Sindh, Rajasthan and Haryana) some 1500 years ago – long after Indo-European languages became well established in Europe and elsewhere. So as they migrated west, did they carry the typical genetic signature of the First Indians? Yes, they did.

According to a study titled 'Reconstructing the Indian Origin and Dispersal of the European Roma: A Maternal Genetic Perspective' published in 2011:[1]

> [T]wo different groups of lineages could be distinguished among the Roma. The European/Middle Eastern haplogroups accounted for 65% to 94% in different Roma groups, whereas the rest of the lineages belonged to haplogroup M. This last haplogroup is common in East Africa and Asia, but is rarely found in Europe.[2] Within haplogroup

---

[1] I. Mendizabel, et al., 'Reconstructing the Indian Origin and Dispersal of the European Roma: A Maternal Genetic Perspective', *PLOS One* (January 2011).

[2] The presence of mtDNA haplogroup M1 in Africa is thought to be the result of back-migration from Asia.

M, all lineages were of clear Asian origin except one East African M1a1 sequence found in two Portuguese Roma. The main Asian subhaplogroups found were M5a1, M18 and M35b, which have been reported to have an Indian origin.

In other words, when there was an emigration of people from the Indian subcontinent towards the west and all the way to Europe, a genetic signature indeed went with them – of the descendants of the first inhabitants of south Asia: the deep-rooted maternal haplogroup M, which is 'rarely found in Europe'. Since the Romas couldn't have introduced Indo-European languages to Europe and since there is no other significant genetic south Asian signature in Europe or central Asia, we have to consider the case for Out of India as closed.

This takes us to the next question: if migrations into India led to the spread of Indo-European languages in the Indian subcontinent, when did they happen, and where did the migrants come from?

Genetic signature of the 'Aryans'

This question, which has vexed scholars and animated partisans for over a century, is now being settled by genetic evidence made possible by new techniques for extracting and analysing ancient DNA which allow us to see how people moved and how demography changed over time. By analysing ancient DNA from the same location at different periods, or from the same period at different locations, geneticists can answer what changed when.

But before exploring further the question regarding the migration of Indo-European-language speakers to India, let us take a step back and answer a variant of the question that we asked while discussing the Out of India hypothesis: if Indo-European languages are spread over a large area of Eurasia, is there a genetic signature visible across this geography? Yes, there is: the Y-chromosome haplogroup R1a or, more specifically, its subclade R1a-M417, which accounts for almost all the R1a lineages in the world today. A map of R1a-M417 distribution would show it extending from Scandinavia to south Asia, covering almost all of the Indo-European-language-speaking world.

Can we look more closely at R1a-M417 and see how it is distributed around the world? Yes, we can, and this is what it shows. R1a-M417 split into two groups, R1a-Z282 and R1a-Z93, around 3800 BCE, with very different distribution patterns. R1a-Z282 is seen only in Europe, while R1a-Z93 is seen in parts of central Asia and south Asia and accounts for almost all the R1a lineages in India. The difference is strikingly huge. A study titled 'The Phylogenetic and Geographic Structure of Y-Chromosome Haplogroup R1a', published in 2014 and lead-authored by Dr Peter A. Underhill, the world's best-known authority on Y-chromosome, says: 'Of the 1693 European R1a-M417 samples, more than 96% were assigned to R1a-Z282, whereas 98.4% of the 490 Central and South Asian R1a lineages belonged to R1a-Z93, consistent with the previously proposed trend.' To recap, R1a-M417 is the Y-chromosome haplogroup most closely connected with the widest range of Indo-European-language-speaking regions, and its subclade R1a-Z93 is what accounts for almost all of the R1a lineage in India, while its brother-clade R1a-Z282 accounts for almost all of the R1a lineage in Europe.

So do we know where in the world the earliest evidence for R1a-M417 and its subclade R1a-Z93 has been found? Yes, we do. The oldest R1a-M417 was found in Ukraine, dated to between 5000 BCE and 3500 BCE, as reported in the paper 'The Genomic History of Southeastern Europe', published in 2017. It was also discovered in Samara, Russia, dated to around 2800 BCE, and in many places in eastern Europe, dated to around 2500 BCE.

The subclade R1a-Z93 common in India has been found in many central Asian Steppe samples that date to as early as 2500 BCE. In fact, during the middle-to-late Bronze Age (between 2000 BCE and 1400 BCE), R1a-Z93 had a frequency as high as 68 per cent in the central Asian Steppe, according to a study discussed in detail in the next section. The inescapable conclusion, therefore, is that the R1a-Z93 population in India came somewhere from the Eurasian Steppe region.

But how do we know that R1a and its subgroups are linked to Indo-European-language speakers in India? There is an easy way to check: look at the distribution of R1a among Indian population groups and see if they are linked to the traditional custodians of the Sanskrit language, the upper castes in general or the Brahmins in particular. Many studies have repeatedly shown that there is much higher prevalence of R1a among the upper castes than the lower castes and that it is about twice as high among the Brahmins as among the scheduled castes and the scheduled tribes. So what we see is a genetic signature that is prevalent among Indo-European-language-speaking countries and that also has a strikingly elevated presence among the traditional custodians of the oldest layer of Indo-European languages in India: Sanskrit.

Steppe migrations: Step by step

The study that put the question of Indo-European-language speakers migrating to India to rest was released as recently as on 31 March 2018, and was titled 'The Genomic Formation of South and Central Asia'. This path-breaking work that for the first time had access to ancient DNA from south Asia, Kazakhstan and eastern Iran, and its galaxy of eminent authors, was discussed in detail in chapter 2 (pp. 91–97). So here we will limit our recap of that study to parts that deal specifically with 'Aryan' migration.

The study says there was indeed a southward migration of pastoralists from the Kazakh Steppe – first towards southern central Asian regions, that is, present-day Turkmenistan, Uzbekistan and Tajikistan, after 2100 BCE; and then towards south Asia throughout the second millennium BCE (2000 BCE to 1000 BCE). On their way, they impacted the Bactria–Margiana Archaeological Complex (BMAC, a civilization that thrived between 2300 BCE and 1700 BCE, centred on the Oxus river and covering today's northern Afghanistan, southern Uzbekistan and western Tajikistan), but mostly bypassed it to move further down towards south Asia. Here they mixed with the existing people of the Harappan Civilization, thus creating one of the two main sources of population in India today: Ancestral North Indians, or ANI, the other being Ancestral South Indians, or ASI, who were formed by the mixing of the people of the Harappan Civilization with the First Indians in southern India around the same time.

The study arrived at these conclusions after detecting signals of the migrations in the ancient DNA. To quote: 'Our analysis shows no evidence of Steppe pastoralist ancestry in groups surrounding BMAC sites prior to 2100 BCE, but suggests that between 2100 to 1700 BCE, the BMAC communities were surrounded by peoples carrying such ancestry.' This shows there was a migration of the people of the Steppe to the BMAC region around 2100 BCE.

Also, as mentioned earlier, among the ancient DNA from BMAC sites – as well as among the ancient DNA from the eastern Iranian site of Shahr-i-Sokhta – the study made some surprising discoveries with major consequences: three outlier individuals dated to between 3100 BCE and 2200 BCE, with an ancestry profile that was unique. Unlike other ancient DNA samples from the same sites, these had 14 to 42 per cent ancestry from the First Indians, in addition to ancestry from Zagros agriculturists. The Harappan Civilization was known to have had contacts with both the BMAC and Shahr-i-Sokhta, so the study concluded that the outlier individuals were recent migrants from there. These individuals, like others around them, had no Steppe ancestry whatsoever. This fits with the view that the Steppe pastoralists started migrating southward only around 2100 BCE.

But the clincher was yet to come. The scientists also had access to ancient DNA from the Swat valley of Pakistan, dated to between 1200 BCE and 1 CE, more than a thousand years later than the Shahr-i-Sokhta and BMAC samples. The Swat valley samples were genetically very similar to the three outliers from Shahr-i-Sokhta and the BMAC and, like them, had ancestry from the First Indians and Zagros agriculturists. But there was one crucial and telling difference: they also had Steppe ancestry of about 22 per cent. The study says: 'This provides direct evidence for Steppe ancestry being integrated into South Asian groups in the second millennium BCE, and is also consistent with the evidence of southward expansions of the Steppe groups through Turan at this time.'

The study then notes that a great majority of the people speaking Indo-European languages in Europe and Asia today carry ancestry that is related to Steppe pastoralists known as the Yamnaya (more on the Yamnaya in the next section). This is in accordance with the long-held theory that the Yamnaya spoke late Proto-Indo-European and that they spread the Indo-European languages both to Europe and to Asia. Earlier genetic studies had documented the westward movement of the Yamnaya into Europe beginning 3000 BCE, but until this study was released there was no direct ancient DNA evidence of the chain of transmission of Steppe ancestry to south Asia. The authors of the study believe that their documentation of large-scale movement of Steppe groups southwards in the second millennium BCE now provides this missing evidence.

There's more. Remember we said the present-day Indian population is a product of the mingling between the ANI [Harappans (First Indians + Zagros agriculturists) + Steppe pastoralists] and ASI (Harappans + First Indians)? When the geneticists tested whether the ANI–ASI mixture model fits 140 present-day population groups in south Asia, ten groups stood out – each of them being poor fits because they had much more than the expected levels of Steppe ancestry. The strongest signals of elevated Steppe ancestry were in two groups that were of traditionally priestly status, expected to be custodians of texts written in Sanskrit. What could explain this? According to the study, one possibility is that the migration of Steppe pastoralists into south Asia created different groups with different proportions of Steppe ancestry. And those with higher levels of Steppe ancestry seem to have had a central role in sustaining or spreading early Vedic culture. Strong rules of endogamy (marrying within one's own community) among some population groups may have resulted in this excess Steppe ancestry persisting to this day.

Who were the Yamnaya?

Now that we know what happened, let us ask who exactly these Steppe people were that migrated to Europe and to south Asia, spreading their language and leaving a genetic mark on such a large area of the world. The Steppe is a vast region of grasslands, shrublands and savannah that extends from central Europe to China, over an 8000-kilometre stretch that has historically been sparsely inhabited. After the Out of Africa migrants populated much of Eurasia some 50,000 to 35,000 years ago, different regions were inhabited by groups of people who were often isolated from each other by distance and by geographical barriers and who, therefore, grew genetically differentiated from each other. The people who inhabited the Steppe at this time are today classified as Eastern Hunter-Gatherers (EHG) of the Steppe region and Ancient North Eurasians (ANE) of the Siberian region, who are related to the people that migrated to the Americas about 16,000 years ago, through the Bering land bridge.

Then, starting around 5000 BCE there was an influx of people from the Caucasus – the region between the Caspian Sea and the Black Sea that connects west Asia to the Steppe – into the Steppe, resulting in new settlements. The Yamnaya are the result of this influx, and they draw equal ancestry from the Caucasus and the hunter-gatherer population of the Steppe. By around 3700 BCE, the Caucasus region became the centre of the Maikop culture, which seems to have had a strong influence on the Yamnaya. The practice of building 'kurgans' (burial mounds made by heaping stone and earth over a burial chamber, often made of wood) that the Yamnaya are most closely associated with is seen for the first time in the Caucasus, for instance, and it is

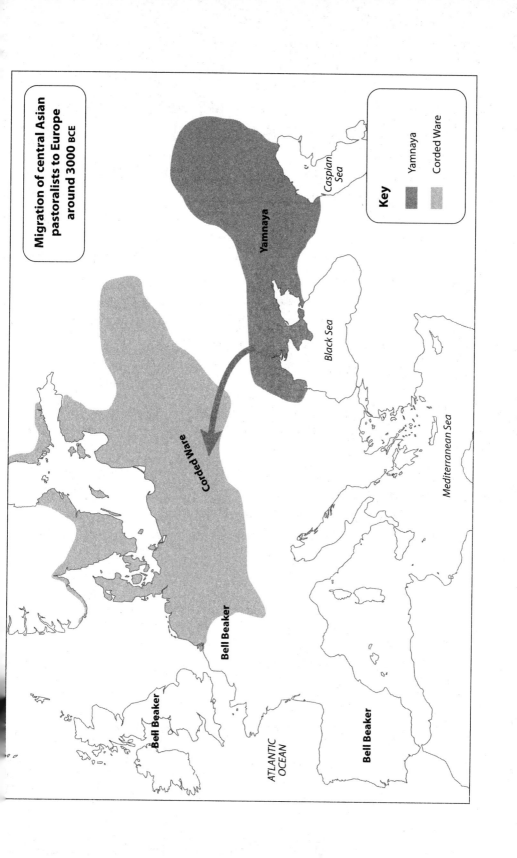

Migration of central Asian pastoralists to Europe around 3000 BCE

Key
Yamnaya
Corded Ware

Yamnaya

Corded Ware

Bell Beaker

Bell Beaker

Bell Beaker

Black Sea

Caspian Sea

Mediterranean Sea

ATLANTIC OCEAN

often argued that the earliest Proto-Indo-European language could have been spoken in the Caucasus before it became the language of the Yamnaya.

There were three technological innovations that the Yamnaya adapted from neighbouring populations such as the Maikop that shaped their role in history: the wheel, the wagon and the horse. We have been unable to zero in on where exactly the wheel was invented because no sooner was it invented than it spread across Eurasia like wildfire. Perhaps it was invented in more than one place at the same time – as we saw in chapter 3, there are clay models of the wheel in the Harappan Civilization dating from before 3000 BCE. The wheel, the wagon and the horse were particularly useful for the Yamnaya because of the geography of their region. Large parts of the Steppe were until then uninhabitable due to a lack of rains that made it unsuitable for agriculture, except along the river valleys, and it had far too few watering holes to maintain large flocks of sheep and cattle.

But with wagons on wheels drawn by oxen or horses, the Yamnaya could take water and supplies with them into the vast Steppe. These draught animals must have enabled the Yamnaya to scale their cattle herding and reap huge productivity gains. From there it would have been but a small step to start trading with cultures such as the Maikop, thereby growing in wealth and influence. That the wagons and horses were crucial to the lives of the Yamnaya is evident from the fact that they were buried with their owners, as seen in the kurgans of the period. The new, mobile lifestyle of the Yamnaya had such an impact on the Steppe that many settlements in the region were abandoned. And the only permanent structures that the Yamnaya themselves left behind wherever they went were their kurgans. In time, owing to the settled communities they traded with, the Yamnaya also mastered the art of metallurgy, a crucial skill for a world of conflict. And conflict was about to break out.

The Yamnaya burst upon Europe around 3000 BCE, a thousand years before their descendants and relatives reached south Asia. In the archaeological record, this new influx into Europe was reflected by a new culture called Corded Ware that started becoming evident from around 2900 BCE. The term 'Corded Ware' refers to a distinctive style of pottery with twisted cord impressions on them, and this culture covered a vast swathe of territory from Switzerland to European Russia. In Germany, ancient DNA showed that people who were buried with Corded Ware pottery drew about 75 per cent of their ancestry from groups related to the Yamnaya and the rest from the farmers who had been the previous inhabitants of the region. The incoming Yamnaya were also responsible for spreading the Bell Beaker culture through much of Europe, even though it did not originate with them. (Bell Beaker refers to a style of distinctive pottery that includes vessels shaped like an upside-down bell.)

In Britain, the incoming Indo-European-language-speaking people with the Bell Beaker culture more or less replaced the earlier people of the island who had built the Stonehenge. 'British and Irish skeletons from the Bronze Age that followed the Beaker period had at most around 10 per cent ancestry from the first farmers of these islands, with the other 90 per cent from people like those associated with the Bell Beaker culture in the Netherlands. This was a population replacement at least as dramatic as the one that accompanied the spread of Corded Ware culture,' writes David Reich in *Who We Are and How We Got Here*.

The Lithuanian–American archaeologist Marija Gimbutas, who was the first to propose the Kurgan Hypothesis in the 1950s (which said that the Proto-Indo-European language was spoken by the people of the kurgan burial culture in the Steppe, the Yamnaya), thought the influx of the Yamnaya into Europe brought about major cultural changes. She said, 'The process of Indo-Europeanization was a cultural, not a physical transformation. It must be understood as a military victory in terms of successfully imposing a new administrative system, language and religion upon the indigenous groups.'

Gimbutas characterized the nature of transition from the Mediterranean cult of the Mother Goddess to a patriarchal society and the worship of the warlike Thunderer (Zeus, Daeus) as violent. Even though her Kurgan Hypothesis has more or less stood the test of time, her characterization of the transition in such stark terms is contested by many who believe it was more gradual and peaceful. The migrations, in their view, were not a concerted military operation, but a gradual expansion of many different tribes and cultures, over many generations. The criticism of Gimbutas has merit, but there is a valorization of violence and a male-centredness that is noticeable in the cultures the new migrants created – their burial mounds had mostly males, often with evidence of great wounds, and many graves contained impressive battleaxes.

There is also genetic evidence for the fact that the Yamnaya expansions were male centred. According to David Reich:

The Y-chromosomes that the Yamnaya carried were nearly all of a few types, which shows that a limited number of males must have been extraordinarily successful in spreading their genes. In contrast, in their mitochondrial DNA, the Yamnaya had more diverse sequences . . . The Yamnaya expansion also cannot have been entirely friendly, as is clear from the fact that the proportion of Y chromosomes of Steppe origin in both western Europe and India today is much larger than the proportion of the rest of genome. This preponderance of male ancestry coming from the Steppe implies that male descendants of the Yamnaya with political or social power were more successful at competing for local mates than local groups.

Reich takes the example of Iberia in far south-western Europe, where Yamnaya-derived ancestry arrived suddenly between 2500 BCE and 2000 BCE. Based on ancient DNA from this period, it was found that approximately 30 per cent of the Iberian population was replaced with the arrival of Steppe ancestry. But the replacement of Y chromosomes was much more dramatic, writes Reich, adding: 'In our data, around 90 per cent of males who carry Yamnaya ancestry have a Y-chromosome type of Steppe origin that was absent in Iberia prior to that time. It is clear that there were extraordinary hierarchies and imbalances in power at work in the expansions from the Steppe.'

Genetics cannot answer what manner of force was used to ensure that local Iberian males left few children behind in comparison to the newly arrived Yamnaya males. Were they killed, driven away or just marginalized? We do not know. Genetics can only show what the result was: the substantial elimination of the local males from the genetic pool.

East, west and east again

Around the same time as they were pouring into Europe, the Yamnaya also sped east across the Steppe to the Minusinsk basin and the Altai mountains in south Siberia, to create there what came to be known as the Afanasievo culture, probably speaking an early version of Tocharian, an extinct Indo-European language. But a more crucial expansion from the south Asian perspective came after the Yamnaya went into western Europe and created the Corded Ware culture. Genetic evidence suggests there was then an 'eastward reflux' back beyond the Urals of western Russia after 3000 BCE, carrying the typical Corded Ware genetic mixture of Yamnaya and European Middle Neolithic (Europe_MN) farmers. By around 2600 BCE, the Yamnaya had splintered into many different successor cultures, from Corded Ware and Sintashta to Srubnaya and Andronovo across the vast Steppe, each one with its own unique style and practices.

A study titled 'Population Genomics of Bronze Age Eurasia' published in *Nature* in June 2015 says, 'From the beginning of 2000 BC, a new class of master artisans known as the Sintashta culture

A summary of west Eurasian migrations into India

Key

Eurasian Steppe

Labels on map:

ATLANTIC OCEAN

EUROPE

Corded Ware Culture

Bell Beaker Culture

Yamnaya pastoralists spread west after 3000 BCE ②

Balkan Mts

Black Sea

Caucasus

Taurus Mts

Mediterranean Sea

AFRICA

Caspian Sea

El Burz Mts

Zagros Mts

Persian Gulf

Arabian Sea

IRAN

Iranian agriculture spreads east after 7000 BCE ①

BMAC

Gonur

AFGHANISTAN

Shahr-i-Sokhta

2000–1500 BCE

Hindu Kush

Indus

Harappa

Ancestral North Indians

Ganga

H i m a l a y a

Ancestral South Indians

Bay of Bengal

KAZAKHSTAN

Inner Asian Mountain Corridor

Altai Mts

ASIA

Yamnaya pastoralists spread east after 3000 BCE ③

emerged in the Urals, building chariots, breeding and training horses, and producing sophisticated new weapons. These innovations quickly spread across Europe and into Asia where they appeared to give rise to the Andronovo culture.' Both the Sintashta and the Andronovo cultures are of relevance to the migration of Steppe people to south Asia, as documented by David W. Anthony, the American professor of anthropology who specializes in Indo-European history and languages.

In *The Horse, the Wheel and Language*, Anthony explores in detail the similarities between the rituals uncovered during excavations at the Russian archaeological sites of Sintashta and Arkaim and those described in the Rigveda – the earliest of the Vedas, variously dated to sometime between 1700 BCE and 1100 BCE,[3] though there is no unanimity on whether parts of it were composed by the 'Aryans' before they reached India. The similarities go to buttress the argument that the 'Aryans' who composed the Vedas and brought Indo-European languages to India were related to the people who left behind evidence of their cultural practices in places like Sintashta and Arkaim.

To quote Anthony:

> The parallels include a reference in Rigveda 10.18 to a kurgan ('let them ... bury death in this hill'), a roofed burial chamber supported with posts ('let the fathers hold up this pillar for you'), and with shored walls ('I shore up the earth all around you; let me not injure you as I lay down this clod of earth'). This is a precise description of Sintashta ... grave pits, which had wooden plank roots supported by timber posts and plank shoring walls. The horse sacrifice at a royal funeral is described in Rigveda 1.162: 'Keep the limbs undamaged and place them in the proper pattern. Cut them apart, calling out

---

[3] Michael Witzel, Wales professor of Sanskrit at Harvard University and an authority on the oldest texts of India, dates the Rigveda between 1400 BCE and 1000 BCE (D.N. Jha, 'Mitanni Indo-Aryan Mazda and the Date of the Rigveda', in *The Complex Heritage of Early India, Essays in Memory of R.S. Sharma* [Manohar Publications, 2014]).

piece by piece.' The horse sacrifices in Sintashta . . . graves match this description, with the lower legs of horses carefully cut apart at the joints and placed in and over the grave.

Anthony describes a Srubnaya site excavated by him that contained surprising evidence of the connection between archaeological evidence in the Steppe and the myths of Indians and Iranians.[4] The evidence related to the mid-winter New Year's sacrifice and initiation ceremony, held on the winter solstice. Anthony writes:

> Many Indo-European myths and rituals contained references to this event. One of its functions was to initiate young men into the warrior category and its principal symbol was the dog or wolf. Dogs represented death; multiple dogs or a multi-headed dog guarded the entrance to the Afterworld. At initiation, death came to both the old year and boyhood identities, and as boys became warriors, they would feed the dogs of death. In the Rigveda, the oath brotherhood of warriors that performed sacrifices at midwinter were called the Vratyas, who also were called dog-priests. The ceremonies associated with them featured many contests, including poetry recitation and chariot races. At the Srubnaya settlement of Krasnosamarskoe in the Samara river valley, we found the remains of a late bronze age midwinter dog sacrifice . . . dated about 1750 BCE . . . At least 18 dogs were butchered, probably more.

Anthony says the chariot-building, stronghold-based chiefdoms of Sintashta armed themselves with new kinds of weapons, created a new style of funeral rituals that involved spectacular public displays

---

[4] Indo-Iranians are that branch of Indo-European-language-speaking Steppe pastoralists who called themselves 'Aryans' and migrated towards southern Asia, ultimately settling in Iran and India. Their culture and myths, as depicted in the Zend-Avesta, the primary religious text of Zoroastrianism, and the Rigveda, the earliest of the Sanskrit Vedas, are similar in many ways.

of wealth and generosity and began to mine and produce metals on a scale previously unimagined in the Steppe. Sometime around 2000 BCE, they finally broke through – or went around – the Ural mountains and spread eastward across the Steppe. He writes, 'With them went the eastern daughters of Sintashta, the offspring who would later emerge into history as the Iranians and the Vedic Aryans. These eastern and southern connections finally brought northern Steppe cultures into face-to-face contact with the old civilizations of Asia.'

Anthony wrote his book with the backing of archaeological data, mostly. But now, ancient DNA has shown that he was on the mark. 'The Genomic Formation of South and Central Asia' confirmed that between 2000 BCE and 1400 BCE, a vast region of the eastern European and trans-Ural Steppe had a relatively homogeneous population that was different from those who populated the region earlier. The distinguishing feature of this population was ancestry from the European farmer. The 'eastward reflux' that was mentioned earlier, carrying the genetic mixture of the Corded Ware culture, was now common across the Steppe.

But there's a further distinction. As you move farther east, to present-day Kazakhstan and as far as the Minusinsk basin in Russia, the ancient DNA samples reflect the addition of another ancestry that the 2018 genomic formation study calls West Siberian Haplogroup or West Siberian_HG. This shows that as the 'eastern reflux' reached Kazakhstan and farther east, it encountered and mixed with a population that already had a West Siberian_HG ancestral component. So the study created a new group, Steppe-MLBA_East, to separate it from the Steppe-MLBA_West, with no such ancestry.

This is important for us because it is probably this Steppe-MLBA_East that finally moved south from the Steppe to the BMAC and Turan, and then farther south to the Indian subcontinent. The genetic study characterizes the Steppe influx into south Asia only as Steppe-MLBA, since both MLBA_West and MLBA_East fit as sources for Indian ancestry. But it is likely that MLBA_East is what reached south Asia since it is geographically much closer to the subcontinent. The strong presence of R1a-Z93 – the Y-chromosome haplogroup of Steppe origin found in India – in Kazakhstan is another reason.

Does the study take us any closer to the date of the 'Aryan' migration into south Asia? In many ways, it does. Since the BMAC ancient DNA shows Steppe presence only after 2100 BCE and is conspicuously absent before that, it is clear that a Steppe migration to south Asia through this route could not have happened earlier. Considering that the BMAC isn't very far from south Asia and that it had had strong trade relations with the Harappans, it couldn't have been much later either. There is existing archaeological evidence that suggests that migrations towards south Asia from the BMAC may have started happening soon after. The first non-controversial evidence for the horse in the Harappan region comes from Pirak in Balochistan, and it is dated to 1800 BCE, in the Late Harappan phase. Pirak also had figurines of horses made in terracotta and unburnt clay – remember that there is no representation of the horse in any other Harappan seal or artefact. This means that the first Steppe migrations into the Indian subcontinent could have almost coincided with the decline of the Harappan Civilization.

Parallels between south Asia and Europe

There are unmissable parallels between the history of migrations into south Asia and the history of migrations into western Europe, though they differ in the details. In western Europe, agricultural technology was brought from west Asia by migrating Anatolian agriculturists between 7000 BCE and 5000 BCE. South Asia saw the arrival of Zagros herders around the same time, although it is open to question whether they brought a full-fledged agricultural package with them. As mentioned before, it is possible that early agricultural experiments had already begun in places such as Mehrgarh in Balochistan and Lahuradewa in Uttar Pradesh, and the migrants may only have catalysed the transition to agriculture by bringing in new domesticates. In western Europe, the incoming Anatolian agriculturists and the resident hunter-gatherers mixed in varying degrees and gave birth to many Neolithic cultures. In south Asia, the incoming herders from Zagros mixed with the First Indians and went on to create the Harappan Civilization. Europe later saw the arrival of Steppe pastoralists who mixed with the local inhabitants to produce new population groups that created and/or spread the Corded Ware, Bell Beaker and other cultures. In south Asia, the incoming Steppe pastoralists mixed with the Harappans to create the new genetic cluster ANI, while the Harappans mixed with the inhabitants of south India, the direct descendants of the First Indians, to create the new genetic cluster ASI. Both groups mixed again, to varying degrees in different regions and during different periods, to create the population of India as it is today.

There is also a parallel between Europe and south Asia in the gender bias that is reflected in the Steppe migrations, as pointed out by Reich earlier in this chapter. As long as Indian geneticists were only looking at mtDNA of present-day Indians, they could not detect the Steppe migrations. It is only when they began looking at the Y-chromosome ancestry that the reality of Steppe migrations became clear. To quote Reich again: 'The preponderance of male ancestry coming from the Steppe implies that male descendants of the Yamnaya with political or social power were more successful at competing for local mates than local groups . . . It is clear that there were extraordinary hierarchies and imbalances in power at work in the expansions from the Steppe.'

It was the 2017 paper 'A Genetic Chronology for the Indian Subcontinent Points to Heavily Sex-biased Dispersals' that brought attention to this gender disparity in India. The paper said: 'Genetic influx from Central Asia in the Bronze Age was strongly male-driven, consistent with the patriarchal, patrilocal and patrilineal social structure attributed to the inferred pastoralist Indo-European society.' The paper also said 70 to 90 per cent of mtDNA lineages of present-day Indian population groups derive from First Indians, while only

10 to 40 per cent of Y-chromosome lineages have similar ancestry. This difference is attributable to the sex bias in the later migrations.

There is one crucial difference between the experiences of western Europe and south Asia with multiple mass migrations. In western Europe, each migration significantly replaced the previous population, while in south Asia, the replacement has been far less on the whole. For example, in many parts of Europe today, the percentage of the original hunter-gatherer ancestry has gone down to single digits, though there are some exceptions in northern Europe. In India, by contrast, the ancestry of the First Indians still constitutes between 50 and 65 per cent for most population groups when you look at the whole genome (as opposed to either Y-chromosome or mtDNA separately).

This difference is also visible in language distribution: 94 per cent of western Europeans today speak an Indo-European language while only about 75 per cent of Indians do so. Dravidian languages are spoken by nearly 20 per cent of Indians, while western Europe has no non-Indo-European language with a similar strong presence.

Interestingly, the only indigenous non-Indo-European language left standing in western Europe today, Basque, is spoken in a region that withstood the massive Steppe migrations into Europe. The Basques draw their ancestry more from the early European farmers – and the hunter-gatherers with whom they mixed – than from the Steppe migrants. Therefore, it is not surprising that they got to retain their pre-Steppe-migration language and culture. (There might be a parallel here with the Dravidian languages of south India in some ways, as both managed to survive in areas that escaped the dominance of the Steppe migrants.)

The ancient DNA evidence for Steppe migrations into Europe took many archaeologists by surprise because after the Second World War they had developed a disdain towards the Nazis and their theories and beliefs, which included the idea that they belonged to the superior and 'pure race' of 'Aryans', unlike the east Europeans or the Jews; that

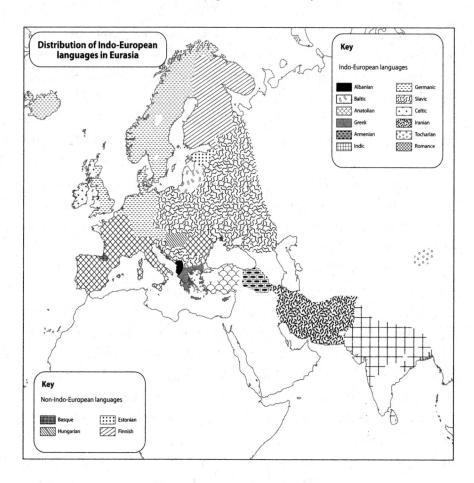

Distribution of Indo-European languages in Eurasia

Key

Indo-European languages

- Albanian
- Baltic
- Anatolian
- Greek
- Armenian
- Indic
- Germanic
- Slavic
- Celtic
- Iranian
- Tocharian
- Romance

Key

Non-Indo-European languages

- Basque
- Hungarian
- Estonian
- Finnish

they had conquered many lands in the past and spread their 'Corded Ware culture'; and that they had, thus, the natural and inherited right to the lands of others around them. As part of this rejection of Nazi ideas, the archaeologists contested the suggestion that Europe in the past had seen invasions or migrations that had brought about culture change. But the new genetic discoveries have disproved both the archaeologists and the Nazis. Unlike what the archaeologists had believed, we now know that migrations did change the culture of Europe. And unlike what the Nazis had believed, the people they called 'Aryans', the Steppe pastoralists, themselves were of mixed ancestry, not a 'pure race' by any stretch of the imagination. More poignantly, they came from eastern Europe, a region that the Nazis had deep contempt for.

Apart from the impulse to dismiss Nazi theories, many archaeologists and historians had other reasons too to doubt mass migrations. For example, the archaeologist Colin Renfrew thought that once farming took off and populations exploded, it would have been difficult for any new migrations to happen on a scale large enough to change the demography of these densely populated regions. So how did the Yamnaya manage to beat the odds?

One explanation is that while populations did increase dramatically when agriculture spread, many regions were not densely inhabited. For example, the highest population estimate for the Mature Harappan Civilization, the largest civilization of its time, was five million – spread over a million square kilometres from Shortughai in Afghanistan to Sutkagan Dor on the Makran coast. And that is less than the population of just one city today: Ahmedabad. In the case of Europe, archaeological evidence suggests that the incoming Yamnaya converted large areas not occupied by European Neolithic farmers from forests to grassland, the kind of geography they were familiar with.

But the possibility of another explanation became apparent when a paper co-authored by the geneticist Eske Willerslev and others in 2015 said they had identified DNA sequences resembling *Yersinia pestis*, the bacterium that causes the plague, in seven ancient individuals out of the 101 they had analysed, taken from Bronze Age Eurasia. The samples belonged to individuals buried in Yamnaya-linked cultures such as Corded Ware, Afanasievo, Sintashta and Andronovo. The study concluded: 'It has recently been demonstrated by ancient genomics that the Bronze Age in Europe and Asia was characterised by large-scale population movements, admixture and replacements, which accompanied profound and archaeologically described social and economic changes. In light of our findings, it is plausible that plague outbreaks could have facilitated – or have been facilitated by – these highly dynamic demographic events.'

If diseases carried by the new influx of people from the Steppe played a part in changing the demography of Europe, it wouldn't be the last time this happened, of course. The diseases carried by the Europeans into the Americas played a significant role in decimating the original population of that continent. Did they play a part in the disappearance of the Harappan Civilization too, which started declining around the same time that the early Steppe migrants reached India? We won't know until we get direct ancient DNA evidence from cities such as Harappa, Mohenjo-daro or Kalibangan from the Late Harappan period. But even if we discover that diseases did play a part in reducing the Harappan population, it is fairly certain that this was not the cause of the decline of the civilization because there is mounting evidence that it was a long period of drought that brought it down – around the same time that it was wrecking other civilizations such as those in Egypt, Mesopotamia and China.

The most exhaustive, multi-year geological study on the possible reasons for the decline of the Harappan Civilization was published in a 2012 paper titled 'Fluvial Landscapes of the Harappan Civilization',[5] which identified a clear cause: a prolonged drought that ultimately made monsoonal rivers go dry or become seasonal, affecting habitability along their courses. To quote: 'Hydroclimatic stress increased the vulnerability of agricultural production supporting Harappan urbanism, leading to settlement downsizing, diversification of crops, and a drastic increase in settlements in the moister monsoon regions of the upper Punjab, Haryana, and Uttar Pradesh.'

This study's finding was confirmed in the strongest way possible when, in July 2018, the International Commission on Stratigraphy (ICS), the official keeper of geologic time, introduced a new age called 'The Meghalayan' which runs from 2200 BCE to the present and which

---

[5] Liviu Giosan, et al., 'Fluvial Landscapes of the Harappan Civilization', *PNAS* (2012).

began with a mega drought that crushed a number of civilizations worldwide – in Egypt, Mesopotamia, China and, of course, India. The mega drought was likely triggered by shifts in ocean and atmospheric circulation.

So in hindsight, it looks like the British archaeologist and director general of the Archaeological Survey of India between 1944 and 1948, Sir Robert Eric Mortimer Wheeler, blamed the wrong person for the disappearance of the Harappan Civilization when he wrote, 'On circumstantial evidence, Indra stands accused!' He was suggesting, of course, that 'invading Aryans' had destroyed the Harappan Civilization – something for which there is no archaeological evidence. He should have looked more in the direction of Varuna, the Lord of Rain![6]

After the decline

It is possible, of course, that the cause for the decline of the Harappan Civilization was not singular, but plural. The long drought may have drained the civilization of its energy and also decimated its trade with Mesopotamia, which was going through its own crisis; the reigning ideology of the Harappan Civilization may have collapsed as a result, leading to the disappearance of the symbols of power and commerce such as the ubiquitous seals and the script; there may have been internal rebellions; the Harappans may have taken the available option of moving to new fertile regions such as the Ganga valley and starting afresh rather than finding new ways of keeping the old system going; and the influx of a new wave of warrior-like migrants from the Eurasian Steppe might have been just the last straw that broke the system for good. But as we will see later, though the Harappan Civilization may have gone into decline by around 1900 BCE, the people did not disappear and neither did the language nor all of the associated cultural beliefs and practices of the largest civilization of its time.

---

[6] On the basis of additional evidence, Sir Robert did later exonerate Indra!

This is because when the civilization dimmed due to the long drought, the Harappans spread out, to both the east and the south, seeking new fertile land and carrying their language, culture and at least some of their practices with them. (See pp. 195–97 for the continuities from the Harappan Civilization.)

The 'Aryans' arrived around this time or a little later with a pastoralist lifestyle, new religious practices such as large sacrificial rituals, a warrior tradition and mastery over the horse and metallurgy. The result was a mixing of populations and the formation of a new power elite that was dominant enough to ultimately force a language shift to Indo-European across northern India. Some of the beliefs and practices of the Harappans reshaped the religious ideology of the 'Aryans' while some other practices would have continued as folk religion and culture at a more popular level.

In the south, the migrating Harappans would have found a more congenial atmosphere for their language and culture, partly because the 'Aryans' had not yet reached peninsular India and, perhaps, partly because of the presence of earlier migrants who may have spread Dravidian languages, as we saw in chapter 3.

In the language of genetics, the Harappans contributed to the formation of the Ancestral South Indians by moving south and mixing with the First Indians of peninsular India and also to the formation of the Ancestral North Indians by mixing with the incoming 'Aryans'. Therefore, in many ways, they are the cultural glue that keeps India together – or the sauce on the pizza, to build on a metaphor that we used earlier.

That the newly dominant elite from the Steppe had a clear preference for a non-urban, mobile lifestyle may be part of the reason why India had to wait for more than a millennium after the Harappan Civilization, for its 'second urbanization' that began after 500 BCE. As Anthony noted in *The Horse, the Wheel and Language*, the Yamnaya were a mobile, pastoral people who caused the near disappearance of settlement sites wherever they came to dominate.

Harappans and the Vedas: Disconnect and connect

When the Steppe migrants reached India, they would have come across a culture that already had its own myths, religious beliefs and practices and dominant language or languages, and was coping with a slowly unfolding disaster caused by the long drought. We do not yet know what different routes the people who called themselves 'Aryans' may have taken, or how many different and competing groups there might have been. What we do know is that the visible disconnect between the Harappan culture as revealed by its archaeological remains and the Indo-European culture as revealed by the Vedas – starting with the earliest composition, the Rigveda – reduces over time.

Here are a few examples of the early disconnect. The main gods and goddesses of the Rigveda – Indra, Agni, Varuna and the Asvins – find no representation in the vast repertoire of Harappan imagery. The converse is also true: the Rigveda is of no help in trying to interpret the dominant symbols and imagery of the Harappan culture – such as the ubiquitous seals that display a unicorn with what looks like a brazier or manger in front; the script; the Great Bath of Mohenjo-daro and its significance; and so on.

In fact, in one instance, the contrast between the Rigvedic principles and Harappan practice is quite striking. The Rigveda denounces 'shishna-deva' (literal meaning: phallus god or phallus worshippers), while Harappan artefacts leave no one in doubt that phallus worship was part of its cultural repertoire. The archaeologist R.S. Bisht, who excavated the most visually stunning Harappan site in India at Dholavira, says there is clear evidence of deliberate destruction of phallic symbols and idols both in Dholavira and other sites after the civilization declined. Book 7, 21.5 of the Rigveda says 'may not the "shishna-deva" approach our holy worship', and Book 10, 99.3 describes how Indra slew them. Some authors have used 'lustful demons' as the appropriate translation for 'shishna-deva' in this context, but the literal meaning of the original text – and, of course, the animosity – is quite clear.

Archaeological Survey of India

Free-standing phallic columns in Dholavira

R.S. Bisht writes in his report on the Dholavira excavation: 'At least six examples of free-standing columns were discovered from the excavations. These free-standing columns are tall . . . and with a top resembling a phallus or they are phallic in nature. That is why most of them were found in an intentionally damaged and smashed condition.' About the Dholavira statue of a seated man the report says:

[It was] perhaps the largest that the Harappans ever attempted . . . It was found upside down as a building block of a wall that was raised by the late Harappans . . . It is made of porous limy sandstone . . . It was in a seating position with a flat base, arms resting on the knees, with both knees drawn up and kept apart as if to show the genitals as the sculpture has shown no feature of clothing.

The statue depicts a male individual and its execution is close to realistic. The belly is shown protruding. The rear portion of the statue also shows evidence of depiction of hair lots falling down, which is also damaged. It was certainly vandalised, possibly just like all the statues, which were found at Mohenjo Daro.

The head portion of this statue is missing now. It seems that its head was intentionally chopped off, elbows and knees are also

Source: Archaeological Survey of India

Top: Statue of a seated man found upside down in the ruins of Dholavira
Bottom: Front and side views of the statue, with its genitals intentionally rubbed off and damaged

considerably damaged. The intentional damage caused to this statue may be a clear indication of the paradigm shift in religious belief and ideology, most probably belonging to the Mature Harappan phase [2600–1900 BCE] as this statue is found from a secondary context belonging to Stage VI [1950–1800 BCE]. The manner in which the statue was damaged clearly indicates that the role played by it could no longer be appreciated by Stage VI occupants. The depiction of nicely cut inscriptions on the seals of Stage VI without any motif may also indicate a departure of beliefs and customs.

Stage VI at Dholavira, dated to beween 1950 BCE and 1800 BCE, is the Late Harappan stage, when the Mature phase of the civilization had ended and the site was even deserted for a while. According to the excavation report, 'Stage VI which appears at the site after a phase of desertion, is equally significant in that it not only brought out many changes of far-reaching consequence in planning, architecture and sigillography [relating to seals] as well as a quantum shift in economic structure, but also witnessed feverish commingling of communities.'

We do not know who or what caused the upheaval in Stage VI at Dholavira; it could have been an internal rebellion during the final stages of the Harappan Civilization for all we know. But the existence of phallic symbols and statues at Harappan sites and the disdain for phallus worship visible in the Rigveda suggest a gap between them.

Bisht is not a proponent of the idea that the Harappan Civilization is not 'Aryan' or 'Vedic'. In fact, he believes that the kind of society that the Rigveda projects is close to what we find at the Harappan sites. However, he also admits that the Vedas looked down upon 'shishna-devas' and that the lack of the horse in the Harappan Civilization is a problem in identifying this civilization as Vedic. Until the Harappan script is deciphered, he thinks, the dispute will continue.

The disconnect between the Harappan world and the world of the earliest Veda is apparent in less ideological and more mundane matters too. For example, the rest of the civilized world at the time knew of

the Harappan Civilization as Meluhha; the Harappans were involved
in the politics of Mesopotamia, even to the extent of taking sides in
their battles; and the economic relationship between Harappa and
Mesopotamia was intimate enough for the Harappans to set up colonies
in places such as the Oman peninsula to facilitate trading and even
mining. But these complex, sophisticated trading activities and urban
relationships do not find reflection in the early Vedic corpus. The world
of the Rigveda and the world that is revealed by the material culture
of Harappa seem two very different universes – and this is without
even bringing up the matter of the horse.

Horse sense on Harappa

The problem of the horse is this: the horse is rarely to be found in
the Harappan Civilization, neither as skeletal remains nor as images
on seals and artefacts, while it is very prominent and ubiquitous in
the Rigveda. So much so that two of the main gods, the Asvins, are
horsemen. Two other deities, Ushas and Agni, are described as riding
horse-drawn chariots. In a hymn, the river Sarasvati is described as
'created vast for victory like a chariot'. In fact, the presence of the
horse in the Rigveda is so prominent that no other animal comes
close. There are five hymns about the horse in the Rigveda, but only
one about the bull, one about the goat and one about a bird. One
of the hymns about the horse (Mandala 1; hymn 162)[7] refers to the
horse sacrifice as follows:

> They who observing that the Horse is ready call out and say, the
> smell is good; remove it;
> And, craving meat, await the distribution, – may their approving
> help promote labour.
> The trial-fork of the flesh-cooking cauldron, the vessels out of which
> the broth is sprinkled,

---

[7] Translation by Ralph T.H. Griffith.

The warming-pots, the covers of the dishes, hooks, carving boards,
– all these attend the Charger.
The starting-place, his place of rest and rolling, the ropes wherewith
the Chargers feet were fastened,
The water that he drank, the food he tasted, – among the Gods,
too, may all these attend thee.
Let not the fire, smoke-chanted, make thee crackle, nor glowing
cauldron smell and break to pieces.
Offered, beloved, approved, and consecrated, – such Charger do
the Gods accept with favour.

For those who do not accept the idea of 'Aryan' migrations and
insist that the 'Aryans' were indigenous, it is axiomatic that the
Harappan Civilization was 'Vedic' – or a creation of the 'Aryans' who
composed the Vedas. They make three arguments for why the lack
of horses or chariots in the Harappan cities should not stand in the
way of a Vedic identity for the civilization. One, horse bones are rare
even in post-Harappan times, even though nobody doubts that horses
were present then. Second, as the archaeologist B.B. Lal, the leading
proponent of the Harappans-as-Vedic-Aryans proposition, puts it: 'A
wooden chariot, or anything wooden, is very difficult to find in the hot
and humid climate of this country. I have not come across anything
wooden, except a piece of grain . . . in Kalibangan.' Point three is that
there has indeed been one internationally verified finding of horse
bones – at the Harappan site of Surkotada in Gujarat – dating back to
between 2100 BCE and 1700 BCE. These bones were indeed examined
by the archaeozoologist Professor Sandor Bokonyi, who had this to
say, 'The occurrence of true horse (*Equus caballus*) was evidenced by
the enamel pattern of the upper and lower cheek and teeth and by the
size and form of the incisors and phalanges (toe bones). Since no wild
horses lived in India in post-Pleistocene times [i.e., after 9700 BCE],
the domestic nature of the Surkotada horse is undoubtful.'

This statement makes two important points. One, there have been no wild horses in India since Pleistocene (which lasted from 2.58 million years ago to 11,700 years ago). Therefore, the horse found at Surkotada has to be a domesticated one, not a wild one. But the corollary to these two statements is that if there were no wild horses in India in the last 11,700 years, then the horse was clearly not domesticated in India, since horse domestication happened no earlier than 3500 BCE. Therefore, the Surkotada horse is either imported or belongs to a breed that was imported, even by Bokonyi's own statement.

Moreover, Bokonyi's verification of the horse bones has itself been strongly challenged by equally respected archaeozoologists such as Richard Meadow. Even if you assume that Bokonyi was right and Meadow was wrong, it still leaves a large gap between the kind of presence the horse wields in the Rigveda and the near complete absence of horse and horse-related imagery in the Harappan culture, especially in the thousands of seals and sealings that portray everything from mythical unicorns to bulls, buffaloes, peacocks, elephants, tigers and rhinoceroses. The hot, humid climate of the country shouldn't stop us from finding steatite seals of horses if they existed.

Theoretically, even the physical presence of a horse or two in the Harappan Civilization should not be surprising since there is historical record of the Harappans exporting Indian animals such as the elephant, water buffalo and the peacock to Mesopotamia, and importing a horse in return from there or elsewhere should raise no eyebrows. But that wouldn't change the overall picture of the serious disconnect between the role the horse plays in the Rigveda and the role it plays – or rather, does not play – in Harappan archaeological record and imagery.

The archaeologist M.K. Dhavalikar had this to say on the Rigveda being clearly post-Harappan when he discussed the issue of the horses and the Vedas:

If you are reading some novel, how will you date it? If there is mention of a mobile there, you will say it was written in the 20th century or later . . . So like that there are two markers in the Rigveda. One is the occurrence of horse. That is very important. Because that is the most favourite animal of the Aryans. It played a role in their religious beliefs also . . . Secondly, the Rigveda also talks about 'ayas', which clearly means copper, because when iron was discovered later, they had to coin a new word, 'krsna ayas' or black copper.

Now on pure archaeological evidence, domestic horse starts appearing from 1900 BCE. That is Late Harappan period, which is 1900 to 1500 BCE. So this is one fixed point – about 1900 or 1800. Iron was here in north India by 1400 to 1500 BCE. So you can safely put Rigveda to be somewhere between 2000 BCE and 1400 BCE.

The earliest Veda, in other words, postdates the Harappan Civilization.[8]

Remnants of a civilization

The Vedic corpus was composed over many centuries, and it is important to remember that the discrepancy between it and the Harappan Civilization reduces over time. The later the Vedic text, the more the likelihood of finding connections to the Harappan cultural heritage. If the Rigveda was antagonistic to, and disdainful of, 'shishna-deva', by the time of the Upanishads, composed between 500 BCE and 100 BCE, this was no longer the case. The number of borrowed words from Dravidian languages is also higher in the later Vedic texts than in the earlier ones. There are many Harappan seals, sealings and terracotta figurines that remind one of yoga, but there are no clear references to yoga in the Rigveda. But by the time of the *Katha Upanishad*, there are explicit references to it. A Harappan seal shows a figure wearing a

---

[8] According to Professor Witzel, since iron appears in the north-western part of the Indian subcontinent (the region first occupied by the 'Aryan' migrants) only around 1000 BCE, the Rigveda could have been composed as late as that.

horned headdress sitting in a yoga-like posture surrounded by animals, and it has been interpreted by some as an early depiction of Siva. Many historians and archaeologists reject this interpretation on the grounds that this is projecting later-day concepts into the distant past. While that may be so, it still leaves open the possibility of a convergence between later-day ideas of an ascetic Siva and the seal images, beliefs and myths of the Harappans.

This is not surprising because over time incoming cultures often do adopt, adapt to and intermingle with existing cultures, and the Aryans and the Harappans may have done the same to varying degrees across cultural domains and geographic regions. And, of course, a lot of the cultural continuity from the Harappan Civilization is reflected in popular practices rather than in the Vedic corpus.

The way houses are built around courtyards; the bullock carts; the importance of bangles and the way they are worn; the manner in which trees are worshipped and the sacredness of the peepul tree in particular; the ubiquitous Indian cooking pot and the kulladh; the cultic significance of the buffalo; designs and motifs in jewellery, pottery and seals; games of dice and an early form of chess (dice and chess-like boards have been found at multiple Harappan sites); the humble lota which is used to wash up even today; and even the practice of applying sindoor and some measurement systems – the ways in which we carry on the traditions of the Harappan Civilization are too many to count.

A vase discovered at the Harappan site of Lothal in Gujarat has a painting that shows a crow standing next to a pitcher with a deer looking back at it, seemingly depicting the tale of the thirsty crow in the Panchatantra. So some of the tales we tell our children may have been the same ones told by the Harappans to their own children.

What ended around 2000 BCE, therefore, was the power structure that had kept the civilization going for over seven centuries, and with it went the script, the seals, the standardized bricks and some of the ideology as well – such as the unicorn. But many other things that are part and parcel of the common man's life continued, along with some of the philosophical and cultural underpinnings of south Asia's first civilization. We may not recognize all of them, but they are the foundation on which our culture, traditions and history stand today.

At the end of a long process of interaction between the Harappans and the 'Aryans', what we see are Indo-European languages replacing the earlier languages across much of northern, western and eastern India and a new syncretic culture emerging with elements recognizable from both the Harappan culture and the Rigveda. Just as the script and seals of the Harappans disappeared into the mist of prehistory, so did some of the early gods and rituals of the Vedas.

The scriptural language of the Aryans, Sanskrit – the language in which one would expect to see the least change, as with all scriptural languages – itself changed to some extent due to its interaction with the Harappan languages. Retroflex consonants (to utter which you have to curl your tongue and strike your palate), which are very rare in Indo-European languages but very common in pre-Aryan Indian languages such as those belonging to the Dravidian language family, made their way into Rigvedic Sanskrit itself. Examples would include pushti, gana, varna and purna. Considering that even Old Iranian, the most closely related language to Sanskrit, has no retroflex consonants, their increasing presence in Sanskrit over time is usually seen as the result of the influence of languages that were prevalent in India before Sanskrit arrived. The Rigveda has a limited number of borrowed words from Dravidian languages, but the number goes up steadily in the later Vedas.[9]

---

[9] According to Professor Witzel of Harvard University, retroflex consonants are a 'cross-language family feature' of north-western India, and are found in eastern Iranian such as Khotanese Saka and Wahi and the language isolate Burushaski, apart from the Dravidian languages. He also points out that out of the 300-odd loan words in the Rigveda, very few are Dravidian.

The Corded Ware example

The emergence of a new culture from the collision between the Harappans and the incoming 'Aryans' is not surprising because that is exactly what happened a thousand years earlier when the Steppe pastoralists streamed into western Europe. The Corded Ware culture in Europe, which is the most striking archaeological signal of the arrival of the Steppe Yamnaya in Europe, was not brought by them from the Steppe. It was the result of the interaction between the Yamnaya and the Neolithic farmers of Europe that they had come into contact with.

This is how David Anthony explains it in *The Horse, the Wheel and Language*:

> The material culture of the Corded Ware horizon was mostly native to northern Europe, but the underlying behaviours were very similar to those of the Yamnaya horizon – the broad adoption of a herding economy based on mobility (using ox-drawn wagons and horses), and a corresponding rise in the ritual prestige and value of livestock.

The defining traits of the Corded Ware horizon were, he writes:

> [A] pastoral, mobile economy that resulted in the near disappearance of settlement sites (much like Yamnaya in the Steppes), the almost universal adoption of funeral rituals involving single graves under mounds (like Yamnaya), the diffusion of stone hammer-axes . . . and the spread of a drinking culture linked to particular kinds of cord-decorated cups and beakers, many of which had local stylistic prototypes . . .

In a paper published in the journal *Antiquity* in 2017, Kristian Kristiansen, professor of archaeology at the University of Gothenburg, Sweden, and three co-authors dug deeper into how the Corded Ware culture came about. The paper dwells on what Steppe migrations to

Europe involved, apart from massive burning down of forests to create Steppe-like grazing lands for the herds. The authors found systematic evidence from multiple burial sites that showed that 'Corded Ware males practiced exogamy [marrying outside one's community], perhaps marriage by abduction', since many of the women buried in the graves were of non-local origin, and had a different diet during childhood. This is also supported by genetic evidence that showed more varied mtDNA haplogroups among Corded Ware females than among males.

The study goes on to say:

> Exogamy is a clever, and perhaps necessary, policy if new migrating groups are mainly constituted by males. This is a probable scenario for an expanding pastoral economy, and is supported by archaeological data from the early horizon of the Single Grave/Corded Ware culture in Jutland [in northern Germany and Denmark], where 90 per cent of all burials belonged to males. It gains further support from later historical sources from India to the Baltic and Ireland. They describe, as a typical feature of these societies, the formation of warrior youth bands consisting of boys from 12–13 up to 18–19 years of age, when they were ready to enter the ranks of fully grown warriors. Such youthful war-bands were led by a senior male, and they were often named 'Black Youth' or given names of dogs and wolves as part of their initiation rituals.

According to Kristiansen and his co-authors, pastoral economies that are more warlike and mobile tend to dominate agrarian economies. Organized bands of young males from pastoralist societies go out to settle in new territories, often taking wives from farming cultures forcibly.

The paper examines how the typical Corded Ware pottery came into being. The authors say the Yamnaya did not have a strong tradition of pottery making because their mobile lifestyle required using things that would not break easily and could be transported without difficulty in their wagons. For example, they usually made containers using leather, wood or the bark of trees.

So in the burials of the earliest Corded Ware culture, there is no typical Corded Ware pottery. It appeared only later in northern Europe, and the study says the reason for this was that Corded Ware pottery began only after women with ceramic skills married into the incoming Yamnaya culture and then began making ceramic ware that imitates the leather, wooden and woven containers of the Yamnaya. The confirmation of this theory, says the study, comes from the archaeological find of a well-preseved flat bowl with short feet made of wood (which can be used for turning milk into yogurt or other dairy products overnight). The ceramic version of this wooden utensil became a typical example of Corded Ware pottery across Europe.

The precise ways in which an incoming people and culture engage with an existing people and their culture would, obviously, differ across time and space. However, it would be reasonable to assume that there would be some common threads between the massive Steppe migrations into Europe and India, considering the shared customs and practices of the migrants.

For example, King Bhoja's eleventh century CE treatise on the use of Sanskrit for poetic and rhetoric compositions, 'Sarasvatikantabharana' (Necklace of Sarasvati) says, 'the language of the uncultured is not to be (shown as) used at sacrificial rites; one should not (show anyone) speaking anything but Prakrit to women; nor mixed language to high-born people, nor Sanskrit to the uneducated.'[10]

The injunction against poetic compositions showing anyone speaking to women in anything other than Prakrit is perhaps a congealed convention that evolved out of a concern for realism, because women may have often belonged to a different, non-'Aryan', language

---

[10] Sheldon Pollock, *The Language of the Gods in the World of Men* (Permanent Black, 2006).

culture than the 'high-born' or 'Aryan' men from the Steppes they were married to in the early period of the migrations.

A multi-source civilization, not a single-source one

Both in India and in Europe, the Indo-European-language speakers were the last migrants significant enough to change the demography. India has seen multiple incursions since then – from Alexander's army in 326 BCE to the Sakas or the Scythians around 150 BCE, the Huns around 450 CE, the Arabs in 710 CE, the Mughals in 1526 CE, and then the Portuguese, the French, the Dutch and the British – but none of them have left more than a delicate and small impression on our demography, although their impact on our culture has often been bigger. This we can say now with certainty thanks to DNA and the science of genetics. And no migration or invasion is likely to change our demography in the future either. Hence the name of this chapter: The Last Migrants. Our common history has been about creating a unique culture that draws its elements from multiple traditions and experiences. We are a multi-source civilization, not a single-source one.

By the time the last migrants, the 'Aryans', arrived sometime after 2000 BCE, Indians in the subcontinent were already one of the largest modern human populations on earth (if not *the* largest); had already led an agricultural revolution and then an urban revolution leading up to the creation of the largest civilization of its time; and were spearheading an agricultural transition in almost every region, in the north, south, east and west. It would be accurate to say that the very foundation of India as we know it was laid during the period of the Harappan Civilization.

The millennium or so that followed the dimming of the Harappan Civilization would have been the most tumultuous and turbulent period in the history of the modern human in south Asia. But we have very little record of this and hence very little understanding of it. Look at all that happened: a long-standing civilization, the largest of its kind at the time, fell apart due to the ravages of a long drought, and its most visible symbols of power and prestige slowly disappeared even as urbanism itself did; people migrated to the east and the south in search of a new life; a new set of migrants came in from the north-west, bringing new languages and a different culture that put emphasis on sacrificial rituals and prioritized pastoralism and cattle breeding over urban settlements; another set of migrants came in from the north-east, bringing new languages, new domesticated plants and perhaps wetland farming techniques and a new variety of rice . . . and thus the pot of Indian culture was put on the boil. Four thousand years later, it is still simmering, with new ingredients getting added once in a while, from the Jews to the Syrians to the Parsis.

Epilogue

Seeing History the Right Side Up

A subjective commentary on what this book tells us – and an examination of how caste came to be.

Over the four chapters of this book, we saw how the Indian 'pizza' got made, with the base or the foundation being laid about 65,000 years ago, when the Out of Africa migrants reached India. The sauce began to be made when the Zagrosian herders reached Balochistan after 7000 BCE, mixed with the First Indians, and then together went on to build the Harappan Civilization. When the civilization fell apart, the sauce spread all over the subcontinent. Then came the 'Aryans' after 2000 BCE, and cheese was sprinkled all over the pizza, but a lot more in the north than in the south. Around the same time arrived the major toppings which we see today in different regions in different amounts – the Austroasiatic and Tibeto-Burman-language speakers. And then, much later, of course, came the Greeks, the Jews, the Huns, the Sakas, the Parsis, the Syrians, the Mughals, the Portuguese, the British, the Siddis – all of whom have left small marks all over the Indian pizza.

Like all metaphors this is a silly oversimplification, of course, but is useful to the extent that it helps correct deeply embedded and problematic misconceptions about who we are. It is commonly thought that the 'adivasis' or 'original inhabitants' or 'tribals', who form about 8 per cent of the population, are very distant and very different from the rest of the Indian population – a perception that has led to them being looked down upon, not just as people who have chosen to continue a particular lifestyle, but as people who are 'not us'. Now we know this is baseless. The tribals are 'us'.

The tribals share much with the rest of the population genetically since they carry the ancestry of the First Indians and they ought to be seen as the foundational population of India as it is today. As we have seen, 50 to 65 per cent of whole genome ancestry of the Indian population comes from the descendant lineages of the First Indians. And there is no population group in India today that does not carry First Indian ancestry, no matter what language it speaks or where in the caste hierarchy it falls. How appropriate it is then that the most recognizable image of the Harappan Civilization is the 'dancing girl' (cover image) who could very well be a tribal girl. As we saw in chapters 2 and 3, First Indians were a part of that first urban revolution. (Aside: We do not know, of course, whether the girl was 'dancing'; what we do know is that she has a powerfully attractive, insouciant stance that denotes energy and authenticity even today.)

The disdain towards tribals and scheduled castes comes from an inbuilt belief system that 'others' them and now we know why this othering needs to go. This attitude also reflects in the general unconcern for our own prehistorical sites. From Jwalapuram to Bhimbetka to Dholavira, the lack of interest in and identification with these sites is almost as palpable as in the case of our western neighbour's similar indifference to historical sites that predate the arrival of Islam in the subcontinent. We will know that we have matured and owned our past in the full sense when prehistorical sites in India start attracting enough visitors who are excited and thrilled to see what their ancestors did and how they lived.

The second misperception that the pizza metaphor helps correct is about the origins of the common culture that we can experience today across the subcontinent. It is now possible to see that the foundational source for much of this common culture is the mighty Harappan Civilization that lasted seven centuries in its mature form and was the largest one of its time, both in terms of population and area.

Aryavarta and Magadha

Much of what happened in the centuries after the decline of the Harappan Civilization and the arrival of migrants from the Steppe lies in relative archaeological darkness (which is not surprising considering migrating groups of Steppe pastoralists elsewhere were not big on permanent settlements). As mentioned earlier, we do not know what routes the 'Aryan' migrants took, or how many groups there might have been, or for what period the migrations may have continued. But we do know from the early Vedic texts that there were conflicts between Indo-European-language-speaking groups, so multiplicity of migrations is probably a given. Linguistics and now genetics can throw a little more light on the migration process.

According to the 'Grierson hypothesis' that was advanced in the 1930s by Sir George Grierson, compiler of the Linguistic Survey of India, and then built on by Franklin C. Southworth in 2005, Indo-Aryan languages can be subdivided into two sociolinguistic regions, one of them being the 'inner' (or North-Central) and the other being the 'outer' (or Southwestern-Eastern). In this division, the North-Central languages would include Hindi, Punjabi, Rajasthani, Bundeli and Pahari, while Southwestern-Eastern would include Bangla, Bihari, Oriya, Marathi and Konkani). Southworth deals with the subject in a long chapter in *The Linguistic Archaeology of South Asia*, and he says such a division can be accounted for 'by assuming a long, slow influx of Central Asian herding peoples moving into the Indo-Iranian borderlands, to the Punjab and then on the one hand eastwards to

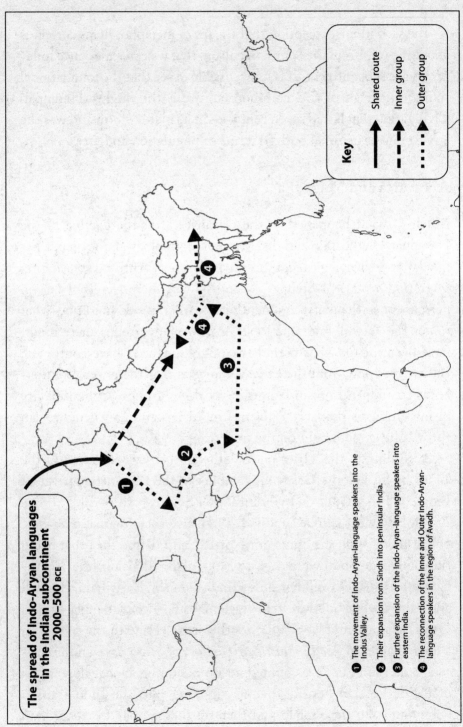

The spread of Indo-Aryan languages in the Indian subcontinent 2000–500 BCE

Key

Shared route

Inner group

Outer group

1 The movement of Indo-Aryan-language speakers into the Indus Valley.

2 Their expansion from Sindh into peninsular India.

3 Further expansion of the Indo-Aryan-language speakers into eastern India.

4 The reconnection of the Inner and Outer Indo-Aryan-language speakers in the region of Avadh.

Adapted from Franklin C. Southworth, Linguistic Archaeology of South Asia, RoutledgeCurzon, 2005

the Ganga, and on the other hand, down the Indus to the Deccan and further east'.

He points out:

> The regional division represented by the North-Central and Southwestern-Eastern languages corresponds to a longstanding historical division between Aryavarta, the land of Hindu orthodoxy, and the regions known as mleccha-desas or barbarian lands, where it was understood that non-Aryan languages were spoken, and Hindu rituals were not observed. Perhaps significantly, this distinction continued to appear in the literature even long after communications had been established between the central and peripheral areas. These two areas are geographically separated by the Vindhyan complex, a continuous chain of mountains, hills and plateaus which stretches across central India. Accounts of the branches of the Yadava clan (a branch of the ancient Indo-Aryan lineage which was reputed to have been tainted by the adoption of local customs) place these people mainly to the south or east of the Vindhyan complex.

('Non-Aryan languages' in the paragraph above do not mean non-Indo-European languages as they are understood today; they only mean languages that fall in the 'outer' region that were considered 'non-Aryan' by the Aryavarta orthodoxy.)

The genetic evidence too suggests that there was indeed a substructure within the 'Aryan' populations that migrated to India, which may correspond to the linguistic substructure pointed out by Grierson and Southworth. This is what the 2018 paper 'The Genomic Formation of South and Central Asia' says on the subject, after noting that ten out of 140 present-day Indian population groups studied had 'significantly elevated' Steppe ancestry:

> We found the strongest two signals [of Steppe ancestry] in Brahmin_ Tiwari and Brahmin_UP and more generally there was a striking

enrichment of signals in groups of traditionally priestly status which
was most notable in northern India . . . The enrichment is striking
as these groups are among the traditional custodians of texts written
in early Sanskrit.

A possible explanation is that the influx of Steppe Middle to
Late Bronze ancestry into South Asia in the mid-2nd millennium
created . . . groups with different proportions of Steppe ancestry, with
one having relatively more Steppe ancestry having a central role in
spreading early Vedic culture.

To paraphrase this in the context of the linguistic evidence, not all
groups of migrating Indo-Europeans had the same social attitudes or
approaches. Some (perhaps belonging to the 'inner groups' to use the
geographical terminology of Grierson) were highly orthodox in their
social relations (and perhaps language use) and genetically mixed less
with the local population, while those belonging to the 'outer groups'
were much less rigid.

This difference that is noticeable in linguistics and genetics is also
noticeable in textual references, especially those relating to 'Aryavarta'
and 'mleccha-desa'. As noted in *Greater Magadha*, written by Johannes
Bronkhorst, emeritus professor of Sanskrit and Indian Studies at the
University of Lausanne, the grammarian Patanjali asks an interesting
question and then answers it himself in his commentary *Mahabhasya*,
written around 150 BCE: 'Which is the land of the Aryas? It is the
region to the east of where the Sarasvati disappears, west of the Kalaka
forest, south of the Himalayas, and north of the Pariyatra mountains.'
The Kalaka forest is traditionally assumed to be near the confluence
of the Ganga and the Yamuna, and the Pariyatra mountains to be the
Vindhyas, since many other records mention Aryavarta as the land
between the Ganga and the Yamuna.

'The passage from Patanjali's Mahabhasya occurs in virtually
identical form in some other texts, viz., the Baudhyana Dharma Sutra
and the Vasistha Dharma Sutra,' writes Bronkhorst. He continues:

'Both these texts add that, according to some, Aryavarta is the land between the Ganga and the Yamuna, which supports the idea that the Kalaka forest was indeed situated at or near the confluence of these two rivers. Olivelle . . . argues that these two Dharma Sutras are later than Patanjali. If this is correct, it supports the view that the region east of the confluence of the Ganga and the Yamuna was still more or less foreign territory for many Brahmins even after Patanjali.'

Note that this definition of Aryavarta roughly corresponds with the 'inner' linguistic group in the North-Central region as defined by Grierson and Southworth, as opposed to the 'outer' linguistic group of the Southwestern-Eastern region. Remember that when Patanjali was defining the land of the 'Aryas', the areas to its east were already occupied by Indo-European-language speakers and, in fact, these regions were the major centre of the second urbanization of India that began around 500 BCE, much after the decline of the Harappan Civilization. The first Indian empire, that of the Mauryas (322–180 BCE), had also arisen in this region, outside of the closely defined Aryavarta. This was the region called Magadha that gave rise to both Jainism and Buddhism between the seventh and fifth centuries BCE. (Buddhism is dated to between the sixth and fourth centuries BCE and Jainsim to between the seventh and fifth centuries BCE.) Both these religions challenged the existing scriptures, sacrificial rituals and social orthodoxy.

What accounts for the aversion that the elite of Aryavarta had for the mleccha-desas? This is how Bronkhorst sees it:

According to the passages cited above, the region east of the confluence of the Ganga and the Yamuna was not considered Brahmanical territory at the time of Patanjali. This does not exclude that there were Brahmins living there. Rather, it suggests that the Brahmins living in it did not receive the esteem which they deemed themselves entitled to. In Patanjali's Aryavarta, on the other hand, we may assume that they did receive this esteem, at least to some extent.

The Brahmins' predominant social position in this region allows us to use the expressions 'Brahmanical society' or 'Vedic society' for the period during which Vedic texts were still being composed. These expressions do not, of course, imply that all members of this society were Brahmins, even less that they were all Brahmins who performed Vedic rituals.

The defining characteristic of Brahmanical society would have been large sacrificial rituals involving substantial gifts to the priestly class and a close and symbiotic relationship between the rulers and the Brahmins.

According to Bronkhorst, the political history of the Ganga valley east of the Ganga–Yamuna confluence supports the idea that this region was not the ideal Brahmanical society.

It is here that the foundations were laid for the Mauryan empire that came to cover a large part of the South Asian subcontinent. If our sources can be believed, none of the rulers involved were especially interested in the Brahmins and their ideas. The early kings of Magadha – Srenika Bimbisara and Ajatasatru – were claimed as their own by Buddhists as well as by Jainas. The Nandas, who consolidated imperial power at Pataliputra around 350 BCE, appear to have become zealous patrons of the Jainas. Chandragupta Maurya overthrew the Nandas, but may have had no more interest in the Brahmins than those whom he replaced. He himself is said to have converted to Jainism and died a Jaina saint. His son Bindusara patronized non-Brahmanical movements, particularly the Ajivikas. His son Asoka was interested in Buddhism; his immediate successors in Ajivikism and Jainism. It is only with the Sungas, who were Brahmins themselves, that Brahmins may have begun to occupy the place in society which they thought was rightfully theirs. This happened around 185 BCE. Forty or fifty years later, as we have seen, Patanjali the grammarian was still not ready to look upon the Ganges valley east of the confluence with the Jumna as being part of the land of the Aryas.[1]

This view of Magadha did ultimately change, of course, as Bronkhorst notes. In the *Manava Dharma Shastra* or *Manusmriti* written sometime before the third century CE, Aryavarta was defined as ranging from sea to sea: 'The land between the same mountain ranges [i.e., Himalaya and Vindhya] extending from the eastern to the western sea is what the wise call "Aryavarta" – the land of the Aryas.' Somewhere between the composition of the *Mahabhasya* and the *Manusmriti*, the ideology of Magadha had perhaps changed enough for the elite of Aryavarta to consider it as their own. We will come back to this soon.

The difference between the inner and outer traditions might explain why the caste system fell into place when it did – and only when it did. The theory that incoming 'Aryans' imposed the caste system on the population when they arrived in the subcontinent has been proved wrong by a genetic study published in 2013 titled 'Genetic Evidence for Recent Population Mixture in India'. It was co-authored by Priya Moorjani, Kumarasamy Thangaraj, Lalji Singh, David Reich and others.

The results of the study that these scientists had conducted, based on genome-wide data from seventy-three population groups in the Indian subcontinent, were stunning. The study showed that between 2200 BCE and 100 CE, there was extensive admixture between the different Indian populations with the result that almost all Indians had acquired First Indian, Harappan and Steppe ancestries, though, of course, to varying degrees. The paper says,

---

[1] 'It is perhaps no coincidence that Pusyamitra, the Sunga general who killed the last Maurya and created the Sunga dynasty, settled, if Kalidasa's *Malavikagnimitra* can be trusted, not in Pataliputra, but far from it, in Vidisa,' writes Bronkhorst.

'India experienced a demographic transformation several thousands of years ago, from a region in which major population mixture was common to one in which mixture even between closely related groups became rare because of a shift to endogamy [marrying within the community].'

We have already seen how, when the Harappan Civilization began declining, as a consequence of the long drought and the arrival of new migrants, there were large-scale population movements from the north-west to both south and east, and much intermixing. So that is not surprising, even though the study reveals that the mixing was quite deep-going: 'nearly all groups experienced major mixture in the last few thousand years, including tribal groups like Bhil, Chamar and Kallar that might be expected to be more isolated'.

What is surprising, because it is counter-intuitive, is that the mixing came to an end sometime around 100 CE. One can imagine two separate groups who had maintained their genetic distance for a long time suddenly deciding that enough was enough and starting to mix. But it is more difficult to visualize groups that had already been mixing waking up one day and deciding to put a stop to it, and creating barriers to continued intermixing. The genetic study says that this is exactly what happened. It was as if around 100 CE a new ideology, which had gained ground and power, imposed on the society new social restrictions and a new way of life. It was social engineering on a scale never attempted before or after, and it succeeded wildly, going by the results of genetic research.

The study links the sudden downing of the shutters on intermixing to the beginning of the caste system: 'The four-class (varna) system, comprised of Brahmanas, Kshatriyas, Vaisyas, and Sudras, is mentioned only in the part of the Rigveda that was likely to have been composed later. The caste (jati) system of endogamous groups having specific social or occupational roles is not mentioned in the Rigveda at all and is referred to only in texts composed centuries after the Rigveda.'

Could the end of the Maurya empire in the closing centuries of the first millennium BCE have had anything to do with this change in ideology? Did the defeat of the Mauryas also presage the eventual disappearance of Buddhism from the subcontinent and the decline of Jainism? Could the orthodox traditions of Aryavarta – with a more rigid view of social hierarchy and opposition towards 'varnasankalana', or mixing between different classes or races – have defeated the more open, freewheeling, progressive and anti-ritualistic ideologies of Magadha that had posed a challenge to it?

Did the rapid expansion of the Maurya empire into the heartland of Aryavarta between the fourth and second centuries BCE threaten the Brahmanical ideology based on sacrifices, the supremacy of Brahmins and their special relationship with rulers, and did Aryavarta strike back in response? Did they, then, over time, manage to impose their own long-held ideals of 'purity' and strong endogamy on the rest of society, including the Indo-European-language speakers of eastern India, who did not share those ideals, though they called themselves 'Aryans' too? Bronkhorst addresses some of these questions in his book.

A few things follow from this discussion. The caste system in India is *not* coterminous with the arrival of the 'Aryans' in the subcontinent. It fell in place around the ankles of Indian society only about two millennia later. And by the time it came about, intermixing had already taken place to varying degrees. So Ambedkar was right when he stated that the Sudras were not genetically different from the rest of Indian caste society. But perhaps he did not go far enough – he seems to have still considered the tribals to be different from everyone else. We now know that this is not correct – because their genes run through everyone, no matter where in the caste hierarchy one is. Ambedkar was also wrong in denying 'Aryan' migrations altogether, though he cannot be blamed for the mistake since he did not have the genome data that we have today.

The cultural effervescence in eastern India or Magadha began in the centuries before the flowering of the Maurya empire and can be seen in such things as urbanization, new religions and philosophies and the rising affluence and prominence of the trading classes. It had already spread its influence and ideas across the subcontinent and far outside of it too, before the gates of the caste system were installed and closed, perhaps over several generations and centuries, thus turning the country inward in many ways.

A period of achievements and adventures

The five or six centuries before the beginning of the Common Era and a couple of centuries after it would rank as one of the most creative and progressive periods in the history of India. The composition of the Upanishads, the insights and philosophy of which have inspired millions across the world and influenced much of the thought of the Indian subcontinent; the rise of the world's first missionary religions, Jainism and Buddhism, that took the teachings of their founders as well as new linguistic ideas and literary forms to all corners of India and, in the case of Buddhism, to many corners of the then known world; the bringing of east Asia under the spell of Indian cultural ideas; the mesmerizing of China . . . the list is as long as it is exciting. Most of the overseas overtures, outreaches and adventures would have begun either from the eastern or southern parts of India, which would have been without the kind of restrictions on intermixing and voyages across the seas that Aryavarta found necessary to impose.

The momentum of these strong cultural currents carried on for many centuries after a new social hierarchy and a new way of living became common in the subcontinent and mixing between groups of the kind that was seen earlier had become taboo. Sanskrit, as the new language of the elite and the medium of intellectual discourse, probably became more influential than any other language in ancient history, with the possible exception of Latin – and Sanskrit spread more by persuasion and buy-in rather than military invasions as in the case of Latin, as explained beautifully by Sheldon Pollock in his majestic book *The Language of the Gods in the World of Men*. Kings and aspiring kings all over the subcontinent and across the seas in southeast Asia wanted the prestige and comfort that Sanskrit offered, along with its theory of kingship and social structure that seemed to find a ready market among elites everywhere. A powerful body of literature including the two mega epics, the Ramayana and the Mahabharata, which remain unrivalled in their ability to enthrall and inspire, carried in its sinews the new theory of power and social relationships that was perhaps as convincing for those at the receiving end of it as for those at the giving end of it.

This was not inevitable

But there was also a huge social cost to the new social construct, as indicated by genetics, again, as David Reich explains it in *Who We Are and How We Got Here*:

> People tend to think India with its more than 1.3 billion people as having a tremendously large population, and indeed many Indians as well as foreigners see it this way. But genetically, this is an incorrect way to view the situation. The Han Chinese are truly a large population. They have been mixing freely for thousands of years. In contrast, there are few if any Indian groups that are demographically very large, and the degree of genetic differentiation among Indian jati groups living side by side in the same village is typically two or three times higher than the genetic differentiation between northern and southern Europeans. The truth is that India is composed of a large number of small populations.

In essence, the social structure that was imposed in the second century CE has cut the country into 'tukde, tukde' (pieces), to use the vocabulary of television news channel discussions in 2018. When you divide up a people like that, a society's ability to maximize the potential of its individuals is severely affected and, equally importantly, fellow feeling even among people who live in the same locality is dampened, thus aborting the possibility of common actions that would benefit everyone. To what extent this has hampered India, as a nation, is perhaps a question that only sociologists will be able to answer, hopefully quantitatively, some day.

What we know now is that this was not inevitable. This was not the direction in which India was heading till around 100 CE when we seem to have halted suddenly, and turned back on an issue of crucial social importance. It would be wrong to think, though, that the ideological confrontation between what Aryavarta represented – or perhaps what an elite group within it represented and preferred – and what Magadha or eastern India represented and practised came to an abrupt halt. Buddhism kept going for centuries after its defeat in the land of its birth, though its position grew weaker and weaker.

That some of these battles were still being fought seven centuries after the arrival of the caste system in 100 CE we know from the work of Adi Shankara who took on the philosophies of Buddhism and Jainism. We also know this from archaeological and literary sources that have recorded continuing disputation, both intellectual and physical, and from theological movements like Bhakti that gave voice to the voiceless. That Bhimrao Ambedkar chose Buddhism for himself and his followers when he wanted to challenge still existing inequities in the twentieth century shows how the historical threads of a difference of opinion on the way a society ought to be constructed have continued to this day. In this sense, the spectacular ideological confrontation between Mohandas Karamchand Gandhi and Bhimrao Ambedkar too can be seen as a contest between the best of the philosophy of life and society that the conservative Aryavarta had to offer and the best of the rationality and progressivism that Magadha had to offer.

To quote the historian Romila Thapar:

When we assess our cultural heritage, we often tend to forget or we downplay the fact that rationality and scepticism were very much a part of early Indian thought. This was not limited to the Carvaka/Lokayata thinkers but is also clear from some other schools of philosophy, as indeed it is noticeable in Buddhist and Jaina thought. We have inherited a tradition of questioning, which was not limited to philosophical thought but is apparent in popular literature as well. It would be as well to nurture that tradition.

Common questions, multiple answers

If our prehistory should teach us anything, it is that old cliché: unity in diversity. We live in a geographical region that can be termed a common civilizational and conversational area. The topics of our intellectual and cultural discussions, debates and disputes are uniquely our own but we do not have a consensual set of answers: our answers and responses are dependent upon the different traditions and historical experiences that different groups among us carry. We as Indians have lived through the same history too, but we have experienced some of it from different ends. The difference in political or even eating preferences between southern and eastern India on the one hand, and northern and western India on the other hand, are a reflection of the kind of differences that there are, and some of them are deep-going.

Take, for example, our food habits. It is clear that north Indians and western Indians consume far more milk and milk products and far less meat and fish than east Indians or south Indians. Politicians and commentators often look at these differences as sociopolitical in nature. But these have a more foundational reason: genes. Or more specifically, a gene mutation called 13910T which originated in Europe some 7500 years ago. This gene allows the human body to digest milk beyond infancy, into adulthood. *Homo sapiens* are the only mammals in the world who have acquired this ability. This is not surprising because

before humans figured out they could keep cattle or goats and exploit
them for milk, such a mutation would have been unnecessary. But once
they started domesticating cattle, the ability to digest milk as adults
would have became tremendously useful, and a mutated gene that fit
the bill was selected over time by evolution.

The ability to digest milk even into adulthood evolved more than
once, in four different areas of the world. But the European mutation
13910T is of particular interest to us because most Indians who have
the ability to consume milk as adults carry this European version.
A countrywide screening of DNA samples from all major language
groups and regions of India[2] to answer questions about lactase
persistence (the technical term for the ability to digest milk after
infancy) came to many conclusions, three of which are as follows: first,
its distribution in India follows a general north-west to south-east
declining pattern. Second, the mutation is identical to the European
one. Third, only about a fifth of Indians can digest milk into adulthood,
with people in western and northern India being the most likely to do
so. The frequency of the gene ranges from over 40 per cent in certain
parts of western and northern India to less than 1 per cent in parts of
north-east India.

So this finally clarifies why east Indians or south Indians drink far
less milk than north and west Indians. As adults, many of them are
unable to digest it. It bears repeating that all children can consume
milk, whether they have the gene or not. The difference between
those who have the gene and those who do not is that while those
with the gene can go on drinking and digesting milk for the rest of
their lives, others will lose this ability sometime between their first
year and adulthood.

What has all this got to do with vegetarianism, or the relative
difference in consumption of meat and fish between the north and

---

[2] Irene Gallago Romero, et al., 'Herders of Indian and European Cattle Share Their
Predomiant Allele for Lactase Persistence', *Molecular Biology and Evolution* (2012).

west on the one hand and south and east on the other? It is simply this: the ability to digest milk as adults gives those Indians with the gene mutation an option to substitute milk for meat or fish as a source of animal protein, which many of them seem to have taken. This is borne out by surveys of household consumer expenditure carried out by the National Sample Survey. These figures show that, by and large, states consuming a lot more milk consume a lot less meat, fish and eggs, while states consuming a lot more meat, fish and eggs consume a lot less milk.

Clearly, there is a trade-off happening here between milk and meat, but only in some regions. Please also note that regions consuming more milk and less meat are precisely those with a greater prevalence of the gene mutation, and vice versa.

What the gene story tells us is that there are good reasons behind the patterns we see on India's sociological map and for the differing answers given to common questions of our civilization, including what to eat and what not to eat. To try to erase these differences and patterns to create a monoculture would be a typically un-Indian enterprise, prone to mishaps and doomed to failure.

One reason for the continuing and doomed attempt to force-fit an artificial uniformity on Indian culture is the way our history is written, often with justification. Until now, it made sense for history books to begin at that point in time when records became available and to ignore the earlier parts or, at most, dismiss them in a few paragraphs or pages. In India, this meant that everyone began to consider the beginning of our history to be around 4500 years ago, when the Harappan Civilization reached its mature stage, or perhaps when the Vedas were composed centuries later (with a lot many people wrongly conflating these two events). This was understandable because until recently there was no easy way of confirming what went on in prehistory and all that anyone could do was make intelligent guesses. But this is rapidly changing, in India and elsewhere, thanks to ancient DNA. As more and more of it is accessed and analysed all across Eurasia, we are gaining a more granular understanding of our own prehistory and the time has come to begin writing our history from where it should begin – with the arrival of modern humans in India some 65,000 years ago. History, if it is to be undistorted and connected with the people of the country, should be built the right side up: starting with the base, the foundation of our population today, the First Indians.

This shouldn't be difficult. The genius of our civilization, during its best periods, has been inclusion, not exclusion. The Harappan Civilization was built by a population with the shared ancestry of First Indians and the early agriculturists of the Zagros region in Iran. When Buddhist missionaries first carried India's cultural ethos beyond its borders to China, south-east Asia and central Asia, it was driven by a missionary zeal that was global and all-encompassing, without discrimination of caste, creed or race. It drew its principles and practices from all parts of India's previous history including that of the 'Aryans', even while challenging rituals, sacrificial practices and ideas of hierarchy. It was, therefore, natural that Buddhism became the first philosophy in the world that felt the burning desire to share its insights and message of compassion with all humans, without regard for man-made or natural borders. That the Buddha's message still flourishes, with 488 million adherents around the world trying to live up to the principles he enunciated, is testimony to the global appeal of a uniquely Indian philosophy, rooted in the same soil from which the Upanishads grew and drawing sustenance from the same impulses.

The two opposing views of India's history – 'the unchanging India' that was somehow stuck in a bad place without knowing how to move on, as Karl Marx saw it, or an India that has degraded over time from the Vedic perfection of 'time immemorial' – are both wrong and based on misperceptions. India has been ever-changing, not unchanging, and its story is definitely not one of decline. India's history has been dynamic, as full of energy and full of contention as any lively society's history would be – and this, despite the dead weight of casteism that we have carried for two millennia.

So who are we Indians, really?

The best way we can define ourselves is as a multi-source civilization, not a single-source one, drawing its cultural impulses, its traditions and its practices from a variety of heredities and migration histories. The Out of Africa migrants, the fearless pioneering explorers who reached this land around sixty-five millennia ago and whose lineages still form the bedrock of our population; those who arrived from west Asia and contributed to the agricultural revolution and the building of the Harappan Civilization which then became the crucible for new practices, concepts and the Dravidian languages that enrich much of our culture today; those who came from east Asia, bringing with them new languages and plants and farming techniques; and those who migrated here from central Asia, carrying an early version of what would become a great language, Sanskrit, and all its associated beliefs and practices that have reshaped our society in fundamental ways; and those who came even later seeking refuge or for conquest or for trade, and then chose to stay – all have mingled and contributed to this civilization we call Indian. We are all Indians. And we are all migrants.

Appendix

The Valley of the Ghaggar–Hakra

Despite the mounting ancient DNA evidence for migrations from the Eurasian Steppes that changed the demography in a vast region extending from Europe to South Asia, there are some who insist that the story of the 'Aryan' migrations is a vast conspiracy spanning multiple generations, continents and scientific disciplines. One of their main arguments is built around identifying the mighty river Sarasvati mentioned in the Rigveda with the rain-fed, mostly dry, seasonal river Ghaggar that originates in the foothills of the Shivalik Hills and flows through Punjab, Haryana and Rajasthan before going across to Cholistan and then Sindh, both in Pakistan. The river is mostly known as Ghaggar in India, and Hakra after that. It is commonly accepted today that there were a large number of Harappan settlements in the valley of the Ghaggar–Hakra and that the Harappan Civilization is best described as being based on two river systems – the Indus and the Ghaggar–Hakra.

From here on, this is how the argument of the migration denialists goes: Ghaggar–Hakra is indeed the ancient Sarasvati because it fits neatly into the geographic description of the ancient river in the Rigveda as lying between the Yamuna and the Sutlej. Sarasvati became the weak, seasonal stream that it is today only because sometime around

2000 BCE tectonic activity diverted the Himalayan snowmelt that used to flow into it. One tectonic event diverted the Sutlej, which used to flow into the Sarasvati/Ghaggar–Hakra, and made it join the river Beas and then both together flowed into the Indus. The other tectonic event caused a terrace to rise in the Himalayas, diverting glacial waters away from the Sarasvati and into the Yamuna.

This enfeeblement of the Sarasvati is what caused the decline of the large number of Harappan settlements all along the Sarasvati basin – from Rakhigarhi and Kalibangan in India to Ganweriwala in Pakistan – and, consequently, the end of the Harappan Civilization itself. But since the Rigveda talks about the Sarasvati in glowing terms, and refers to it as a 'mighty river' that is 'powerful enough to break mountaintops', the Vedic people must have been present in the Sarasvati valley when the river had not yet lost its power and that means they must have been there during Harappan times. And, therefore, the Vedic people are the Harappans.

This may look like a thin argument to put up against all the evidence for Steppe migrations into Europe and south Asia, but it is an argument that has got attention because of the epic resonance of the name of the river Sarasvati. However, there are serious problems with the argument. Let us go through them one by one.

To begin with, there is no certainty that the Sarasvati described as 'mighty' and 'powerful enough to break mountaintops' in the Rigveda is the one in India and not the Harahvaiti river in Afghanistan which the 'Aryans' may have become familiar with on their journey into India through Afghanistan. (It is a common practice for the letter 'h' in Indo-Aryan to be interchanged with the letter 's' in Indo-Iranian and vice versa, well-known examples being 'Hindu' becoming 'Sindhu' and 'Sapta Sindhu' becoming 'Hapta Hindu'. So Harahvaiti and Sarasvati are virtually the same name.) Today, Harahvaiti is known as Arghandab, the main tributary of the Helmand, a Himalayan snowmelt-fed river. Helmand is indeed a 'mighty river powerful enough to break mountaintops'. It is also possible that the name of the river in

Afghanistan that the 'Aryans' came across first was later transferred to a more feeble, rain-fed river now known as Ghaggar–Hakra lying between the Sutlej and the Yamuna, and the descriptions of the later Sarasvati in the Rigveda are written from a composite memory. Names of favourite heroes, rivers and places keep cropping up many times all over India, after all. There are also several rivers in India today that take their name from Sarasvati.[1]

But there are other big problems too: the Sarasvati or Ghaggar–Hakra seems to have dried up not once, but many times. There is no sanctity to the date of 2000 BCE for when the river Sarasvati was 'enfeebled'. This is so even according to Robert Raikes, the internationally acclaimed hydrologist whose name is often quoted by those who equate the Vedic people with the Harappans. In 1968 Raikes studied the major Harappan site Kalibangan near the Ghaggar–Hakra and wrote a paper for the academic journal *Antiquity*, titled 'Kalibangan: Death from Natural Causes'. Raikes says that the abandonment of Kalibangan was caused by the drying up of the river, but then goes on to write: 'The general hypothesis, which emerges from the calculations that form part of the full article, and from the archaeological evidence that fits so neatly into the picture, is of alternating capture of the Yamuna by the Indus and Ganges systems respectively.' In other words, in the low-lying delta between the Indus and the Ganga, Raikes sees the waters flowing into the Ganga through the Yamuna, or into the Indus through the Sarasvati and the Sutlej, at different periods. He then furnishes a table that shows five alternating diversions of water to the Indus and the Ganga between 2500 BCE and 500 CE, the diversion that caused the abandonment of Kalibangan being only one of them. So even if the 'Aryans' were indeed describing today's Ghaggar–Hakra as the Sarasvati in the Rigveda, it does not necessarily mean this was based on observations made before 2000 BCE, during the Harappan period,

---

[1] The remarkable book *The Vedic People* by Professor Rajesh Kochhar deals with this issue of Sarasvati and Harahvaiti extensively.

because the Ghaggar–Hakra river could have been alive during periods even after the decline of the Harappan Civilization.

The archaeologist V.N. Mishra also made the same assessment, based on his study of sites distribution in the Sarasvati valley. He wrote in 1993:

> All this evidence shows that the hydrological history of the Ghaggar-Hakra is a highly complex one, suggesting that the shifting of the Sutlej and Yamuna courses into and away from the Ghaggar Hakra was neither a unique nor a simultaneous event; instead it took place in multiple episodes . . .
>
> In the light of new data, it can be stated with certainty that both Sutlej and the Yamuna flowed in the Ghaggar bed in the past, during the period of the Harappa civilization as well as before and after it.

In other words, the date of the last drying up of the Sarasvati/ Ghaggar–Hakra remains wide open, and it cannot be used to claim that the Rigveda was composed before the Harappan Civilization declined – the Vedic people could have been on the banks of a river they called Sarasvati much after the end of the Harappan Civilization.

But could the Ghaggar–Hakra have been a 'mighty' river during Vedic times? Michael Witzel, Wales Professor of Sanskrit at Harvard University, points out a difficulty. The migration denialists believe the Sarasvati dried up in part because of a tectonic event that caused the Sutlej, which earlier used to flow into the Sarasvati, to join the Beas and then flow into the Indus. But in Hymn 33, Book Three, of the Rigveda, the Sutlej is described as joining the Beas and then flowing together. This means that by the time the Rigveda was composed, the Sarasvati had already lost the Sutlej waters to the Indus, assuming that it had them earlier. It could not, therefore, have been a 'mighty river that could break mountaintops'. Here's a part of the hymn that describes the Sutlej joining the Beas, as translated by T.R. Griffith. (Vipas is the Vedic name for the Beas and Sutudri is the Vedic name for the Sutlej):

Forth from the bosom of the mountains, eager as two swift mares
with loosened rein contending,
Like two bright mother cows who lick their youngling, Vipas and
Sutudri speed down their waters.
Impelled by Indra whom ye pray to urge you, ye move as 'twere on
chariots to the ocean.
Flowing together, swelling with your billows, O lucid streams, each
of you seeks the other

(As for the waters of the Yamuna flowing into the Ghaggar–Hakra,
if they did so, then the Rigveda wouldn't be mentioning the Yamuna
as a separate river. The 'Yamuna' would then 'be' the 'Sarasvati'. That
the Yamuna is listed as a river separate from the Sarasvati is proof that
if the Yamuna did steal the waters of the Sarasvati to give it to the
Ganga, it happened before the Rigveda was composed.)

Witzel quotes the surveys made by the Pakistani archaeologist
Muhammad Rafiq Mughal which showed there were settlements on
the Pakistani side of the Sarasvati even as late as 1500 BCE, suggesting
that the river was still flowing then, well after the decline of the
Harappan Civilization.[2]

The inferences mentioned above were based on philological and
archaeological evidence and a limited number of geological studies and,
therefore, it would make sense to take stock of two extensive scientific
studies undertaken recently: a 2012 paper titled 'Fluvial Landscapes of
the Harappan Civilization' and a 2017 paper titled 'Counter-intuitive
Influence of Himalayan River Morphodynamics on Indus Civilization
Urban Settlements'. The first was co-authored by the geologists Liviu
Giosan of the Woods Hole Geographic Oceanographic Institution,
Massachusetts, Peter D. Clift of the University of Aberdeen, UK,

---

[2] Mughal is the archaeologist who discovered the numerous Harappan settlements in
Cholistan in the Ghaggar–Hakra valley which today allows us to confirm that the
Harappan Civilization was based on two river systems, the Indus and the Ghaggar–
Hakra.

the archaeobotanist Dorian Q. Fuller and others. The second was co-authored by the geologists Ajit Singh and Rajiv Singh of the Indian Institute of Technology, Kanpur, Kristina J. Thomsen of the Centre for Nuclear Technologies of the Technical University of Denmark and others.

The first study looked at climatic and river flow changes during the Harappan Civilization to understand probable causes for its decline, and came to two clear conclusions. First, a gradual decrease in flood intensity probably stimulated intensive agriculture initially and encouraged urbanization around 2500 BCE. However, continued decline in monsoon precipitation adversely affected both flood-based and rain-based farming ultimately. The second conclusion was about Ghaggar–Hakra:

> Contrary to earlier assumptions that a large glacier-fed Himalayan river, identified by some with the mythical Sarasvati, watered the Harappan heartland on the interfluve between the Indus and Ganges basins, we show that only monsoonal-fed rivers were active there during the Holocene. As the monsoon weakened, monsoonal rivers gradually dried or became seasonal, affecting habitability along their courses. Hydroclimatic stress increased the vulnerability of agricultural production supporting Harappan urbanism, leading to settlement downsizing, diversification of crops, and a drastic increase in settlements in the moister monsoon regions of the upper Punjab, Haryana, and Uttar Pradesh.

In other words, from about 10,000 BCE onward, Ghaggar–Hakra has been a rain-fed river and, therefore, couldn't have been the 'mighty river' that was powerful enough to 'break mountaintops' like a snowmelt-fed river would be.

The second study, by Ajit Singh and others, came to an equally strong conclusion: the Indus Civilization settlements developed along an abandoned river valley, not an active Himalayan one. It states:

Using optically stimulated luminescence dating of sand grains, we demonstrate that flow of the Sutlej in this course terminated considerably earlier than Indus occupation, with diversion to its present course complete shortly after around 8000 years ago. Indus urban settlements thus developed along an abandoned river valley rather than an active Himalayan river . . . We suggest that this abandoned incised valley was an ideal site for urban development because of its relative stability compared to Himalayan river channel belts that regularly experience devastating floods and lateral channel migration.

Even after the diversion of the Sutlej, says the study, ephemeral monsoon-fed rivers deriving from the Himalayan foothills – much like the modern-day Ghaggar – continued to flow in the relict valley, thus helping sustain the Indus urban settlements. The study noted sedimentation in the valley decreasing after 3000 BCE, probably due to reducing monsoon intensity.

'In conclusion,' says the study, 'our results firmly rule out the existence of a Himalayan-fed river that nourished Indus Civilization settlements along the Ghaggar-Hakra palaeochannel. Instead, the relict Sutlej valley acted to focus monsoon-fed seasonal river flow as evidenced by very fine-grained sediments in the upper part of the valley-fill record.'

On the question whether it was the weakening of the Indian summer monsoon that led to the decline of the civilization, the 2017 study is non-committal unlike the 2012 one. It states, 'While independent climate records provide strong evidence for widespread weakening of the Indian summer monsoon across large parts of India 4,200 to 4,000 years ago, and our cores indicate a marked decrease in sedimentation rate after 5,000 years ago, current fluvial chronologies lack the resolution necessary to draw robust conclusions.'

However, the 2012 study's findings that a long-term weakening of the monsoon is what caused the drying up of the Ghaggar–Hakra got a big thumbs-up in July 2018 when the International Commission on Stratigraphy (ICS), the official keeper of geologic time, introduced a new age called the Meghalayan, which runs from 2200 BCE to the present. This is significant because according to the ICS, the Meghalayan age began with a mega drought that crushed a number of civilizations worldwide – in Egypt, Mesopotamia, China and, of course, India. The mega drought was likely triggered by shifts in ocean and atmospheric circulation.

For the ICS to approve a classification of this kind, there has to be clear and unambiguous evidence of a shift of some kind that is global in extent. In the case of the Meghalayan, the evidence is a perturbation in the isotopes of oxygen atoms present in the layers of a stalagmite growing from the floor of the Mawmluh cave in Meghalaya. Professor Mike Walkar of the University of Wales, UK, who led the international team of Holocene scientists responsible for developing the proposal for a new age, told a news agency that 'the isotopic shift reflects a 20 to 30 per cent decrease in monsoon rainfall'.

The overwhelming evidence today, therefore, is that what shrunk the Ghaggar–Hakra was not a tectonic event that stole its waters and gave it to the Ganga or the Indus, but a mega drought that had global impact. To reiterate, the Ghaggar was a monsoon-fed river that was weakened by monsoon failure, and not a mighty, snowmelt-fed river that was used to 'breaking mountaintops' as migration denialists insist.

Bibliography

Anthony, David W. *The Horse, the Wheel and Language: How Bronze-Age Riders from the Eurasian Steppes Shaped the Modern World.* Princeton University Press, 2007.

Bellwood, Peter. *First Farmers: The Origins of Agricultural Societies.* Blackwell Publishing, 2005.

———. *First Migrants: Ancient Migration in Global Perspective.* Wiley Blackwell, 2013.

Bellwood, Peter, ed. *The Global Prehistory of Human Migration.* John Wiley & Sons, 2013.

Bisht, R.S. *Excavations at Dholavira: 1989–90 to 2004–05.* Archaeological Survey of India, 2015.

Bronkhorst, Johannes. *Greater Magadha: Studies in the Culture of Early India.* Brill, 2007.

Bronkhorst, Johannes, and Madhav M. Deshpande. *Aryan and Non-Aryan in South Asia: Evidence, Interpretation and Ideology.* Manohar Publishers & Distributors, 2012.

Bryant, Edwin F., and Laurie L. Patton, ed. *The Indo-Aryan Controversy: Evidence and Inference in Indian History.* Routledge, 2005.

Cavalli-Sforza, L. Luca, Paolo Menozzi, and Alberto Piazza. *The History and Geography of Human Genes.* Princeton University Press, 1994.

Childe, Gordon V. *Man Makes Himself.* New American Library, 1951.

———. *The Urban Revolution.* Town Planning Review. Liverpool University Press, 1950.

———. *What Happened in History.* Puffin, 1985/1942.

Danino, Michel. *The Lost River: On the Trail of the Sarasvati.* Penguin Books, 2010.

Gimbutas, Marija. *The Prehistory of Eastern Europe, Part One: Mesolithic, Neolithic and Copper Age Cultures in Russia and the Baltic Area.* American School of Prehistoric Research, Harvard University, Peabody Museum, 1956.

Harari, Yuval Noah. *Sapiens: A Brief History of Humankind.* Penguin Random House, 2015.

Joan, Aruz, ed., with Ronald Wallenfels. *Art of the First Cities: The Third Millennium BC from the Mediterranean to the Indus.* Metropolitan Museum of Art, 2003.

Kochhar, Rajesh. *The Vedic People: Their History and Geography.* Orient Blackswan, 2000.

Korisettar, Ravi, ed. *Beyond Stones and More Stones.* Mythic Society, 2017.

Krishnamurti, Bhadriraju. *The Dravidian Languages.* Cambridge University Press, 1998.

Kuz'mina, Elena E. *The Origin of the Indo-Iranians,* edited by J.P. Mallory. Koninklijke Brill NV, 2007.

Lal, B.B. *The Rigvedic People: Invaders, Immigrants or Indigenous? Evidence of Archaeology and Literature.* Aryan Books International, 2015.

———. *The Sarasvati Flows On: The Continuity of Indian Culture.* Aryan Books International, 2002.

Lal, Pranay. *Indica: A Deep Natural History of the Indian Subcontinent.* Penguin Random House India, 2016.

Liverani, Mario. *Uruk: The First City.* Equinox Publishing Ltd, 2016.

Mallory, J.P. *In Search of the Indo-Europeans: Language, Archaeology and Myth.* Thames & Hudson, 1991.

Oppenheimer, Stephen. *Out of Eden: The Peopling of the World.* Constable & Robinson Ltd, 2004.

Ostler, Nicholas. *Empires of the Word: A Language History of the World.* HarperCollins Publishers, 2005.

Parpola, Asko. *The Roots of Hinduism: The Early Aryans and the Indus Civilization.* Oxford University Press, 2015.

Petraglia, Michael, and Bridget Allchin, eds. *The Evolution and History of Human Populations in South Asia.* Vertebrate Paleobiology and Paleoanthropology Series, edited by Eric Delson. Springer, 2007.

Pollock, Sheldon. *The Language of Gods in the World of Men.* Permanent Black, 2006.

Possehl, Gregory L. *The Indus Civilization: A Contemporary Perspective.* Altamira Press, 2002.

Ratnagar, Shereen. *The End of the Great Harappan Tradition.* Manohar Publishers & Distributors, 2000.

——. *Understanding Harappa: Civilization in the Greater Indus Valley.* Tulika Books, 2001.

Reich, David. *Who We Are and How We Got Here: Ancient DNA and the New Science of the Human Past.* Oxford University Press, 2018.

Renfrew, Colin. *Prehistory: Making of the Human Mind.* Weidenfeld & Nicolson, 2007.

Roberts, Alice. *The Incredible Human Journey: The Story of How We Colonised the Planet.* Bloomsbury Publishing, 2009.

Shulman, David. *Tamil: A Biography.* Harvard College, 2016.

Singh, Upinder. *A History of Ancient and Early Medieval India: From the Stone Age to the 12th Century.* Dorling Kindersley India Pvt. Ltd, 2009.

Southworth, Franklin C. *Linguistic Archaeology of South Asia.* RoutledgeCurzon, 2005.

Thapar, Romila. *The Past as Present: Forging Contemporary Identities through History.* Aleph Book Company, 2014.

——. *The Penguin History of Early India: From the Origins to AD 1300.* Penguin Books India, 2003.

Wells, Spencer. *The Journey of Man: A Genetic Odyssey.* Penguin Books, 2002.

Journal articles and scientific papers

Akhilesh, Kumar, et al. 'Early Middle Palaeolithic Culture in India around 385 to 172 ka Reframes Out of Africa Models'. *Nature*, 2018.

Allentoft, Morten E., et al. 'Population Genomics of Bronze Age Eurasia'. *Nature*, June 2015.

Basu, Analabha, Neeta Sarkar-Roy, and Partha P. Majumder. 'Genomic Reconstruction of the History of Extant Populations of India Reveals Five Distinct Ancestral Components and a Complex Structure'. *PNAS*, February 2016.

Bates, J., C.A. Petrie, and R.N. Singh. 'Approaching Rice Domestication in South Asia: New Evidence from Indus Settlements in Northern India'. *Journal of Archaeological Science*, February 2017.

Bednarik, Robert G. 'Palaeolithic Art in India'. *Man and Environment*, January 1993.

Belfer-Cohen, Anna, and Nigel A. Goring-Morris. 'Becoming Farmers: The Inside Story'. *Current Anthropology*, October 2011.

Boivin, Nicole, et al. 'First Farmers in South India: The Role of Internal Processes and External Influences in the Emergence and Transformation of South India's Earliest Settled Societies'. Paper presented at the 'International Seminar on the First Farmers in Global Perspective' in Lucknow, 2006. Published in *Pragdhara* 18.

Clarkson, Chris, et al. 'Human Occupation of Northern Australia by 65,000 Years Ago'. *Nature*, July 2017.

Constantini, Lorenzo. 'The First Farmers in Western Pakistan: The Evidence of the Neolithic Agro-pastoral Settlement of Mehrgarh'. Paper presented at the 'International Seminar on First Farmers in Global Perspective' in Lucknow, January 2006. Published in *Pragdhara* 18.

Daly, Kevin G., et al. 'Ancient Goat Genomes Reveal Mosaic Domestication in the Fertile Crescent'. *Science*, July 2018.

Damgaard, Peter de Barros, et al. 'The First Horse Herders and the Impact of Early Bronze Age Steppe Expansions into Asia'. *Science*, May 2018.

During Caspers, Elisabeth C.L. 'Sumer, Coastal Arabia and the Indus Valley in Protoliterate and Early Dynastic Eras: Supporting Evidence for a Cultural Linkage'. *Journal of the Economic and Social History of the Orient*, 22(2), 1979.

Fuller, Dorian Q. 'Agricultural Origins and Frontiers in South Asia: A Working Synthesis'. Institute of Archaeology, University College of London, 2006.

———. 'Ashmounds and Hilltop Villages: The Search for Early Agriculture in Southern India'. *Archaeology International*, November 2000.

Gallego-Llorente, M., et al. 'The Genetics of an Early Neolithic Pastoralist from the Zagros, Iran'. *Scientific Reports*, May 2016.

Giosan, Liviu, et al. 'Fluvial Landscapes of the Harappan Civilization'. *PNAS*, 2012.

Goring-Morris, Nigel A., and Anna Belfer-Cohen. 'Neolithization Processes in the Levant: The Outer Envelope'. *Current Anthropology*, October 2011.

Gyaneshwer, Chaubey, et al. 'Population Genetic Structure in Indian Austroasiatic Speakers: The Role of Landscape Barriers and Sex-specific Admixture'. *Molecular Biology and Evolution*, February 2011.

Haak, Wolfgang, et al. 'Massive Migration from the Steppe Was a Source for Indo-European Languages in Europe'. *Nature*, June 2015.

Jarrige, Jean-François. 'Mehrgarh Neolithic'. Paper presented at the 'International Seminar on First Farmers in Global Perspective' in Lucknow, 2006. Published in *Pragdhara* 18.

Joseph, Tony. 'How Genetics Is Settling the Aryan Migration Debate'. *The Hindu*, 16 June 2017.

——. 'How We the Indians Came to Be'. *Quint*, 2 April 2018.

——. 'Who Built the Indus Valley Civilization?' *The Hindu*, 23 December 2017.

——. 'Who Were the First Settlers of India'. *The Hindu*, 5 September 2017.

Karmin, Monica, et al. 'A Recent Bottleneck of Y Chromosome Diversity Coincides with a Global Change in Culture'. *Genome Research*, April 2015.

Kenoyer, Jonathan Mark. 'Changing Perspectives of the Indus Civilization: New Discoveries and Challenges'. *Puratattva*, 2011.

——. 'The Harappan State: Was It or Wasn't It?' *Wisconsin Archaeological Reports*, Volume 3, 1994.

Kristiansen, Kristian, et al. 'Re-theorising Mobility and Formation of Culture and Language among the Corded Ware Culture in Europe'. *Antiquity*, April 2017.

Laziridis, Iosif, et al. 'Genomic Insights into the Origin of Farming in the Ancient Near East'. *Nature*, August 2016.

Librado, Pablo, et al. 'The Evolutionary Origin and Genetic Makeup of Domestic Horses'. *Genetics*, October 2016.

Lipson, Mark et al. 'Ancient Genomes Document Multiple Waves of Migration in Southeast Asia Prehistory'. *Science*, 2018.

Madella, Marco, and Dorian Q. Fuller. 'Palaeoecology and the Harappan Civilization of South Asia: A Reconsideration'. *Quaternary Science Reviews*, 2006.

Mahadevan, Iravatham. 'Dravidian Proof of the Indus Script via the Rigveda: A Case Study'. Indus Research Centre, Roja Muthiah Research Library, 2014.

——. 'Early Tamil Epigraphy: From the Earliest Times to the Sixth Century CE'. Central Institute of Classical Tamil, 2014.

——. 'How Did the Great God Get a Blue Neck? A Bilingual Clue to the Indus Script'. *Journal of Tamil Studies*, December 2008.

——. 'Indus Fish Swam in the Great Bath: A New Solution to an Old Riddle'. Indus Research Centre, Roja Muthiah Research Library, August 2011.

——. 'Interpreting the Indus Script: The Dravidian Solution'. Convocation address at the Dravidian University, Kuppam, Andhra Pradesh, February 2015.

Majumder, Partha P. 'The Human Genetic History of South Asia'. *Current Biology*, February 2010.

——. 'Understanding the Aryan Debate: Population Genetics Concepts and Frameworks'. *Current Science*, March 2018.

Majumder, Partha P., and Analabha Basu. 'A Genomic View of the Peopling and Population Structure of India.' *Cold Spring Harbor Perspectives in Biology*, 2015.

Mathieson, Iain, et al. 'Genome-wide Patterns of Selection in 230 Ancient Eurasians'. *Nature*, 2015.

McAlpin, David W. 'Brahui and the Zagrosian Hypothesis'. *Journal of the American Oriental Society*, July 2015.

——. 'Proto-Elamo-Dravidian: The Evidence and Its Implications'. *Transactions of the American Philosophical Society*, 1981.

McColl, Hugh, et al. 'Ancient Genomics Reveals Four Prehistoric Migration Waves into Southeast Asia'. bioRxiv, 2018.

Mellars, Paul, et al. 'Genetic and Archaeological Perspectives on the Initial Modern Human Colonization of Southern Asia'. *PNAS*, 2013.

Mendizabel, I., et al. 'Reconstructing the Indian Origin and Dispersal of the European Roma: A Maternal Genetic Perspective'. *PLOS One*, January 2011.

Misra, V.N. 'Indus Civilization and the Rgvedic Sarasvati'. Proceedings of the 'Twelfth International Conference of the European Association of South Asian Archaeologists' held in Helsinki University, 5–9 July 1993. Suomalainen Tiedeakatemia, 1994.

——. 'The Role of the Rgvedic Sarasvati in the Rise, Growth and Decline of the Indus Civilization'. Annals of the Bhandarkar Oriental Research Institute, 2011. Speech delivered at the Bhandarkar Oriental Research Institute in Pune, 27 August 1998.

Mishra, Sheila, Naveen Chauhan, and Ashok K. Singhvi. 'Continuity of Microblade Technology in the Indian Subcontinent since 45 ka: Implications for the Dispersal of Modern Humans'. *PLOS One*, July 2013.

Moorjani, Priya, et al. 'Genetic Evidence for Recent Population Mixture in India'. *American Journal of Human Genetics*, September 2013.

Narasimhan, Vagheesh, et al. 'The Genomic Formation of South and Central Asia'. bioRxiv, March 2018.

Pagani, Luca, et al. 'An Ethnolinguistic and Genetic Perspective on the Origins of the Dravidian-Speaking Brahui in Pakistan'. *Man in India*, 2017.

Palanichamy, Malliya Gounder, et al. 'West Eurasian mtDNA Lineages in India: An Insight into the Spread of Dravidian Language and the Origins of the Caste System'. *Human Genetics*, March 2015.

Parpola, Asko. 'A Dravidian Solution to the Indus Script Problem'. Kalaignar M. Karunanidhi Classical Tamil Research Endowment Lecture delivered at the World Classical Tamil Conference, Central Institute of Classical Tamil, 25 June 2010.

———. 'Study of the Indus Script'. Paper read at the '50th ICES' Tokyo Session, 19 May 2005.

Petraglia, Michael, et al. 'Population Increase and Environmental Deterioration Correspond with Microlithic Innovations in South Asia ca. 35,000 Years Ago'. *PNAS*, July 2009.

Pickrell, Joseph K., and David Reich. 'Toward a New History and Geography of Human Genes Informed by Ancient DNA'. *Trends in Genetics*, September 2014.

Poznik, David G., et al. 'Punctuated Bursts in Human Male Demography Inferred from 1,244 Worldwide Y-Chromosome Sequences'. *Nature Genetics*, 2016.

Raikes, Robert. 'Kalibangan: Death from Natural Causes'. *Antiquity*, December 1968.

Rasmussen, Simon, et al. 'Early Divergent Strains of *Yersinia pestis* in Eurasia 5000 Years Ago'. *Cell*, October 2015.

Reich, David, et al. 'Reconstructing Indian Population History'. *Nature*, September 2009.

Robert, Patrick, Nicole Boivin, and Michael Petraglia. 'The Sri Lankan "Microlithic" Tradition c. 38,000 to 3,000 Years Ago: Tropical Technologies and Adaptations of *Homo sapiens* at the Southern Edge of Asia'. *Journal of World Prehistory*, June 2015.

Romero, Irene Gallego, et al. 'Herders of Indian and European Cattle Share Their Predominant Allele for Lactase Persistence'. *Molecular Biology and Evolution*, 2012.

Sengupta, Sanghamitra, et al. 'Polarity and Temporality of High Resolution Y-Chromosome Distributions in India Identify Both Indigenous and Exogenous Expansions and Reveal Minor Genetic Influence of Central Asian Pastoralists'. *American Journal of Human Genetics*, February 2006.

Silva, Marina, et al. 'A Genetic Chronology for the Indian Subcontinent Points to Heavily Sex-biased Dispersals'. *BMC Evolutionary Biology*, 2017.

Singh, Ajit, et al. 'Counter-intuitive Influence of Himalayan River Morphodynamics on Indus Civilisation Urban Settlements'. *Nature Communications*, 2017.

Southworth, Franklin C., and David W. McAlpin. 'South Asia: Dravidian Linguistic History'. In *Encyclopedia of Global Human Migration*, Blackwell Publishing Ltd, 2013.

Tewari, Rakesh, et al. 'Early Farming at Lahuradewa'. Paper presented at the 'International Seminar on First Farmers in the Global Perspective' in Lucknow, January 2006. Published in *Pragdhara* 18.

Thakur, B., A. Saxena, and I.B. Singh. 'Paddy Cultivation During Early Holocene: Evidence from Diatoms in Lahuradewa Lake Sediments, Ganga Plain'. *Current Science*, June 2018.

Thangaraj, Kumarasamy, et al. 'In Situ Origin of Deep Rooting Lineages of Mitochondrial Macrohaplogroup M in India'. *BMC Genomics*, June 2006.

Thangaraj, Kumarasamy, et al. 'Reconstructing the Origin of Andaman Islanders'. *Science*, May 2005.

Underhill, Peter, et al. 'The Phylogenetic and Geographic Structure of Y-Chromosome Haplogroup R1a'. *European Journal of Human Genetics*, January 2015.

Wang, Wensheng, et al. 'Genomic Variation in 3,010 Diverse Accessions of Asian Cultivated Rice'. *Nature*, 2018.

Warmuth, Vera, et al. 'Reconstructing the Origin and Spread of Horse Domestication in the Eurasian Steppe'. *PNAS*, May 2012.

Westaway, K.E., et al. 'An Early Modern Human Presence in Sumatra 73,000 to 63,000 Years Ago'. *Nature*, August 2017.

Witzel, Michael. 'Autochthonous Aryans? The Evidence from Old Indian and Iranian Texts'. *Electronic Journal of Vedic Studies* 7-3 (EJVS), 2001.

——. 'The Languages of Harappa'. February 2000. www.people.fas. harvard.edu/~witzel/IndusLang.pdf

Zeder, Melinda. 'The Origins of Agriculture in the Near East'. *Current Anthropology*, October 2011.

Acknowledgements

This section is unusually long because there are so many academics, scientists and experts from fields as diverse as archaeology, genetics, linguistics, epigraphy, philology and history that I need to thank for sharing their knowledge with me over the last six years. In the course of those years, I got to know some of them personally and all of them professionally, through their academic work of decades. If there is anyone whose name should be here but is not, my apologies for the inadvertent omission.

I must begin my acknowledgements by remembering four stalwarts who are no longer with us. India's best-known epigraphist, Dr Iravatham Mahadevan, passed away as this book was going to press. The time I spent with him at his home in Chennai, when we discussed the toughest problem in Indian prehistory that he had been grappling with – Harappan script decipherment – will remain a treasured memory. His leaving at precisely the time when his insights into the nature of Indian civilization are being proved right by latest discoveries is particularly heartbreaking.

Equally unfortunate has been the loss of the eminent archaeologists Professor M.K. Dhavalikar and Professor V.N. Misra, who served, at different times, as directors of the premier institution for archaeology in South Asia, Deccan College, Pune, and the geneticist Professor

Lalji Singh, who was the vice chancellor of Banaras Hindu University (BHU). Both Dhavalikar and Misra welcomed me into their homes in Pune, and shared with me their deep understanding of the Harappan Civilization in a way that reading any number of papers would not have matched. Singh, whom I met at BHU, gave me a glimpse of the potential of genetic science in India.

The doyens of history and archaeology in India – Professor Romila Thapar, who has authored many books that have become the standard bearers for ancient Indian history, and Dr B.B. Lal, former director general of the Archaeological Survey of India (ASI) – were also generous with their time when I met them in Delhi. Thapar pointed me in the right direction early on in my research and with her incisive comments prompted me to rethink my arguments. Lal helped sharpen my understanding of the 'Aryan migration' debate.

The globally renowned philologists and Sanskritists Professor Michael Witzel of Harvard University and Professor Sheldon Pollock of Columbia University were of immense help in the writing of this book. Pollock's groundbreaking works on Sanskrit and my email conversations with him threw new light on our history in the early centuries of the Common Era. Witzel's seminal work on the oldest texts of India, his treatises on critical issues of Indian prehistory and my calls and email exchanges with him provided me with sharp new perspectives. I thank both of them for reading my manuscript and making invaluable suggestions and comments.

As readers would have noticed, much of the ancient DNA research that is rewriting global prehistory is led by Professor David Reich of the Harvard Medical School. His book, his research papers and my interactions with him were crucial points in my journey into our prehistory.

Dr Kumarasamy Thangaraj of the Centre for Cellular and Molecular Biology (CCMB), Hyderabad, was often a co-author or co-director of some of these reports and I had the opportunity to meet him at

CCMB during the early stages of my work. Thangaraj has authored many impactful research papers on Indian population genetics.

Four people deserve special mention for the role they played in shaping this book, directly or indirectly: Professor Ravi Korisettar of Karnatak University, who has done some of the most remarkable work in Indian prehistory; Partha Majumder, geneticist and distinguished professor at the Indian Statistical Institute, Kolkata; Professor Vasant Shinde, director of Deccan College; and Professor Shereen Ratnagar, author of many well-known books on Harappan history.

Ratnagar was always willing to engage and was forthright in her criticisms. Shinde gave me access to the impressive library at Deccan College, Pune. Majumder's work on Indian genetic history was an eye-opener when I began research on this topic. Korisettar made possible my visit to Jwalapuram in Andhra Pradesh's Kurnool district and Sanganakkallu in Karnataka's Bellary district, sites that he excavated. Korisettar is now building a museum dedicated to prehistory in Bellary.

As fascinating to me as these sites in Karnataka and Andhra Pradesh was the lab-cum-office of Shanti Pappu, archaeologist and professor, on the outskirts of Chennai. The decades-long work of Pappu and her team at Attirampakkam has been a remarkably productive one.

Two other archaeologists whom I met were Professor Emeritus K. Paddayya of the Deccan College, who excavated the Hunsgi-Baichbal valley of Karnataka, among other sites; and Dr R.S. Bisht, who excavated the most important Harappan site in India, Dholavira.

The turning point in the making of this book came in June 2017, with my writing of an article for *The Hindu*, titled 'How Genetics Is Settling the Aryan Migration Debate'. There are two people who made that article possible – Professor Martin B. Richards of the University of Huddersfield, UK, a global authority on mtDNA, and Dr Peter Underhill of Stanford University, a global authority on the Y-chromosome. Richards's paper on the genetic chronology for the Indian subcontinent revealed to me past research findings in a new light. Underhill has been at the forefront of many path-breaking discoveries in population genetics. I am thankful to both of them for their generous help.

Vagheesh Narasimhan of Harvard Medical School and lead author of 'The Genomic Formation of South and Central Asia' was of tremendous help to me in understanding the nuances of recent research, and the interconnections between them. Priya Moorjani, now with the University of California, and a lead author of a study on the dating of genetic admixture in India, was another source of insight.

I met the geneticist Dr Niraj Rai, a co-author of the paper on the genomic formation of South and Central Asia, at the Birbal Sahni Institute of Palaeosciences in Lucknow, where he is building a lab that will have the capability to analyse ancient DNA. Rai is today the person most closely working with ancient DNA research in India.

The linguists who were most critical to the writing of this book were Professor Franklin C. Southworth and Dr David W. McAlpin, both of them experts on South Asian languages. I could not have written the chapter on the Harappans without their cooperation. McAlpin, who authored the most comprehensive paper on the link between Dravidian languages and Elamite, spared hours of his time to discuss with me the intricacies of Dravidian and Elamite linguistics and the impact of recent genetic discoveries.

The well-known archaeologist Professor Michael Petraglia was another scientist who was of much and timely help. My conversation with him enabled me to get an understanding of the Out of Africa migrations through Arabia.

Historian and professor, R. Champakalakshmi, whom I met in Chennai, graciously helped me gain a better understanding of South Indian history. Astrophysicist and author of the insightful book *The Vedic People*, Dr Rajesh Kochhar and the geneticist Dr Gyaneshwer Chaubey are among the many others whom I got to interact with in the course of writing this book.

It is important to note here that not all whom I have met have been of the same opinion – many have been at the opposite ends of key debates in Indian prehistory. Which is why it was essential for me to meet or talk with all of them and hear their arguments.

Equally important is this caveat: I place no burden of responsibility for any errors that may have crept into my book on the people whom I met, talked with or relied on in the writing of it. All responsibility for errors, if any, rests solely with me.

There are two people who I have worked with closely for over a decade and to whom I owe a debt of gratitude for their indulgence during critical times in my writing career: Aveek Sarkar, editor emeritus of the Anandabazar Patrika Group, and T.N. Ninan, chairman of *Business Standard*.

Early Indians owes much to the three publications that carried my articles related to the subject in the last couple of years – *The Hindu*, Scroll and Quint. My thanks to their editors.

At every stage of the creation of this book, it has been a pleasure to work with Chiki Sarkar of Juggernaut, who combines professional acumen, unerring judgement and firmness of purpose with an easy charm. A message she sent me last year, after seeing one of my articles in a newspaper, is what set the ball rolling.

My thanks also to non-fiction editor Parth P. Mehrotra, whose judicious observations, patience and gracious professionalism have improved the telling of the story immeasurably.

I owe my thanks to managing editor Jaishree Ram Mohan for her intelligent interventions. Art director Gavin Morris deserves all the credit for the cover which made you buy this book. Copyeditor Cincy Jose's careful eye has caught many errors and inconsistencies. Cartographer Mohammad Hassan has drawn interesting maps that should make it easier for the reader to follow the story.

Last, but not the least, my family.

It was my late father, Professor K.M. Joseph, who opened my eyes to the world of books and ideas.

Some parts of this book were written during a few months that

I spent in Kerala. My mother, Chinnamma Joseph, and my sister, Professor Thankamma Emmanuel, made my stay pleasant and my writing effortless.

These acknowledgements would only be half-done if I did not mention my wife, Sheba. Over the decades, my writing has benefited immensely from her natural meticulousness and clarity of thought. Whenever she has gone through a draft of mine she has thrown light on corners I never knew existed, using just grammar and logic. It was her unflagging interest in the topic and her appreciation of its importance that kept the book going during the years when it seemed it would never be finished. I thank her for the endless hours she has put in, poring over the pages of my manuscript.

My daughter, Khemta, did her part by asking the difficult questions which I have tried to answer with this book.

Index

Amri, 74, 121, 122, 123
Amu Darya. *See* Oxus river
Anatolian ancestry, 94, 133, 181
Anatolian plateau, 78
Ancestral North Indian (ANI), 10, 89,
   96n, 168, 169, 181, 187
Ancestral South Indian (ASI), 10, 89,
   96n, 168, 169, 181, 187
ancient human settlements, 6
Ancient North Eurasians (ANE) of
   the Siberian region, 170
Andaman and Nicobar Islands, 46,
   154
Andronovo, 175, 177, 184
animal domestication. *See* domestication
   of plants and animals
animal husbandry, Harappan
   Civilization, 137
Anthony, David W., 177–79, 187, 198
Arabia, 31, 36, 37, 38, 46. *See also*
   Saudi Arabia
Arabian peninsula, 30, 41, 44–45,
   46, 48
archaeology, 30–31, 53, 132, 136, 139
archaic humans, ix, 17, 18, 31, 43,
   48–51, 51–57, 62
   extinction, 62–63
Ardipithecus ramidus, 18
Argentina, 41
Arkaim, 177
Armorite language, 135
'Aryans', 9–11, 88, 95, 142, 143, 149,
   159
   genetic signature, 165–67
   and Harappan Civilization,
      disconnect, 142, 143–45, 187–
      89, 191–93

the last migrants, 161–201
and the Vedas, 88, 142, 144, 162,
   170, 177, 178, 188, 191, 192,
   197, 212, 219, 223, 224
Aryavarta and Magadha, 205–13
ashmounds tradition, 150
Asian Steppe, 166–67
Asoka, 210
Assam, 154, 158, 159
astronomy, Harappan Civilization
   and Mesopotamian Civilization,
   147–48
Asvins, 188, 192
Atramhasis, 125
Attirampakkam, Tamil Nadu, 50,
   51, 52, 54
Australia, x, 37n, 38–39, 52
   first migrants, 42–44
   modern humans, 46
Austroasiatic languages, xii, 152–59,
   203

Bab el Mandeb, ix, 33, 35–36
Bactria–Margiana Archaeological
   Complex (BMAC), 179–80
   and Harappan Civilization,
      cultural relations, xiii–xiv,
      93–95, 167–69, 180
Bajau, 47
Balakot, 122
Balochistan, x, 65, 68, 99, 101, 121–
   22, 126, 134, 136, 149, 180, 203
Baluchi, 130
Banawali, Pakistan, xi, 122
Bangladesh, 154
bangles, Harappan Civilization, 115
Basque, 182

juggernaut

THE APP FOR INDIAN READERS

Fresh, original books tailored for mobile and for India. Starting at ₹10.

juggernaut.in

1

CRAFTED FOR MOBILE READING

Thought you would never read a book on mobile? Let us prove you wrong.

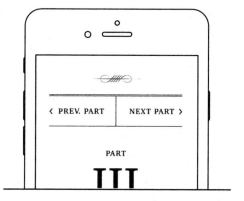

Beautiful Typography

The quality of print transferred
to your mobile. Forget ugly PDFs.

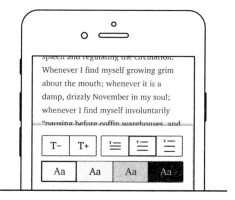

Customizable Reading

Read in the font size, spacing
and background of your liking.

AN EXTENSIVE LIBRARY

Including fresh, new, original Juggernaut books from the likes of Sunny Leone, Praveen Swami, Husain Haqqani, Umera Ahmed, Rujuta Diwekar and lots more. Plus, books from partner publishers and loads of free classics. Whichever genre you like, there's a book waiting for you.

DON'T JUST READ; INTERACT

We're changing the reading experience from passive to active.

Ask authors questions

Get all your answers from the horse's mouth.
Juggernaut authors actually reply to every
question they can.

Rate and review

Let everyone know of your favourite reads or
critique the finer points of a book – you will be
heard in a community of like-minded readers.

Gift books to friends

For a book-lover, there's no nicer gift than
a book personally picked. You can even
do it anonymously if you like.

Enjoy new book formats

Discover serials released in parts over
time, picture books including comics,
and story-bundles at discounted rates.
And coming soon, audiobooks.

juggernaut.in

LOWEST PRICES & ONE-TAP BUYING

Books start at ₹10 with regular discounts and free previews.

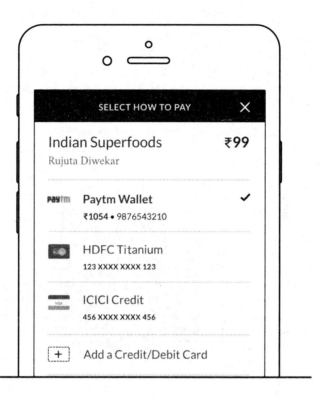

Paytm Wallet, Cards &
Apple Payments

On Android, just add a Paytm Wallet once and
buy any book with one tap. On iOS, pay with one
tap with your iTunes-linked debit/credit card.

Click the QR Code with a QR scanner app
or type the link into the Internet browser
on your phone to download the app.

For our complete catalogue, visit www.juggernaut.in
To submit your book, send a synopsis and two
sample chapters to books@juggernaut.in
For all other queries, write to contact@juggernaut.in